UNDERGROUND TRAIN OVERHAUL

J. Graeme Bruce
OBE, BSc (Eng), FIEE
FIMechE, FCIT

Piers Connor
MCIT

Capital Transport

CW00385191

ISBN 185414 134 1

Published by Capital Transport Publishing
38 Long Elmes, Harrow Weald, Middlesex

Printed by The KPC Group, Ashford, Kent

© J. Graeme Bruce and Piers Connor 1991

CONTENTS

Title Page Upper A variety of cars on their accommodation bogies in the Carbody Shop at Acton Works. Nearest the camera is a Standard Stock car from the Northern Line and, behind it, an Ealing Stock motor car from the Central London Line. In the background, a District Line car is in work. *LT Museum U12552*

Title Page Lower A Standard Tube Stock car from the Northern Line being lifted at Acton Works in 1933. Each car undergoing overhaul was lifted from its service bogies and placed under accommodation bogies at the start of the overhaul cycle to give staff extra working height under the car. *LT Museum U12541*

Left A view of part of the Lifting Shop in April 1951 showing Standard tube and P Stocks. *LT Museum LT56*

Acknowledgements
The preparation of this book could not have been achieved without the help of a number of people. Anthony Bull and Jack Simmonds were especially helpful in the aspect of social changes. Bill Tonkyn and Cyril Birkbeck provided helpful suggestions on the technical and physical changes that have taken place over the years at Acton Works. Bob Greenaway provided a great deal of help, especially with details of the Works after its recent rebuilding. Sheila Taylor provided much help with the tracking down of photographs in the archives of the London Transport Museum, from whom copies of those pictures in this book with a reference number are available for purchase. The photographs on the cover were taken in 1963 and 1990 and are by Alan A. Jackson and Bob Greenaway. Though assistance has been given by past and present London Transport staff, any opinions expressed in this book are those of the authors.

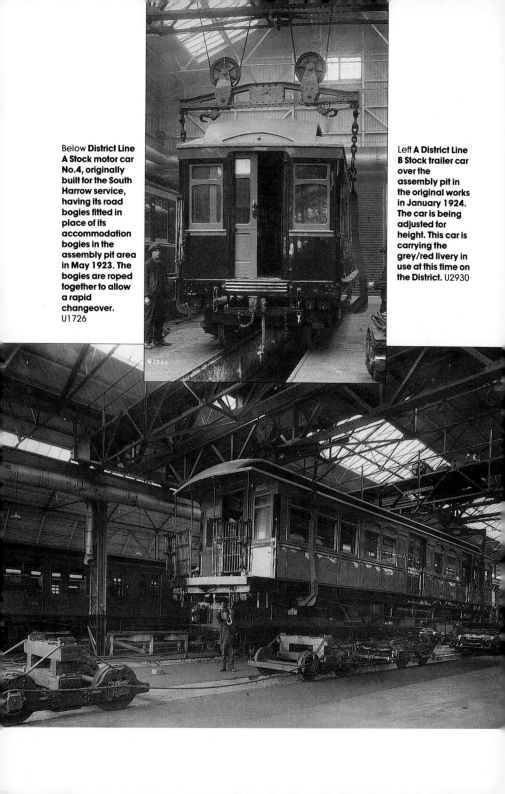

Below **District Line A Stock motor car No.4**, originally built for the South Harrow service, having its road bogies fitted in place of its accommodation bogies in the assembly pit area in May 1923. The bogies are roped together to allow a rapid changeover. U1726

Left **A District Line B Stock trailer car** over the assembly pit in the original works in January 1924. The car is being adjusted for height. This car is carrying the grey/red livery in use at this time on the District. U2930

THE EARLY YEARS

The roots for the provision of a Central Overhaul Works for London's Underground rolling stock go back to the beginning of the century when the American financier Charles Tyson Yerkes formed the Metropolitan District Electric Traction Co Ltd on 15th July 1901 to electrify the steam operated Metropolitan District Railway. Subsequently this company was concerned in promoting and building the Great Northern, Piccadilly Circus and Brompton Railway, better known simply as the Piccadilly tube. The Traction Company also obtained control of the Charing Cross, Euston and Hampstead Railway which had been the focus of Yerkes' original investment interest in London's proposed underground railways.

Neither of these two tube railways had, as yet, been built but a third, the Baker Street and Waterloo, was under construction. Its progress had been delayed due to lack of funds. The Traction Company obtained control of this railway also and, under a financial reorganisation, a company known as the Underground Electric Railways of London Ltd was formed. It was under the jurisdiction of this concern that the Metropolitan District was electrified and the three so-called Yerkes tube lines built.

Yerkes brought technical experts over from America to supervise the equipping of his railways. These experts were under the direction of James R. Chapman, the Chief Engineer. Chapman had been involved in traction work in America, especially the electrification between 1894 and 1901 of the Chicago elevated lines, and he remained with the Underground organisation until 1910. A member of Chapman's team until 1907 was F.W. Ward who was appointed as the equivalent of Rolling Stock Engineer to the group. His name became well known as the patentee, with a Mr Stearn, of the mechanical coupler which became the standard coupling arrangement on Underground passenger rolling stock for over 50 years.

One of the many areas that these American engineers became involved in was the setting up of repair depots for the rolling stock. They also introduced a system of regular maintenance checks, which were set up soon after the start of regular electric services on the District in 1905. The need for these inspections was brought home very soon after electrification when a number of cases of broken axles and cracked truck frames had seriously delayed services. The regular system of inspections was instituted to forestall such mishaps and to minimise future problems with the relatively little understood electrical equipment.

From the beginning, each train was checked every day by the depot staff. Defects noted by drivers during running were dealt with by depot staff at night or between the peak hours. Drivers were penalised for defects found by depot staff which they had missed. Technical defects which the driver noticed when running and which needed immediate attention were dealt with by depot staff called to the train. As the length of lines grew with the extensions of the 1920s and 30s, 'call point' staff supplied from the depots were permanently located at strategic stations along the line to meet trains in service which needed running repairs. The scheme remains in force to this day.

All maintenance was initially carried out on the basis of only repairing damaged equipment or changing worn parts. The daily check was supposed to show what needed doing. However, the problems with wheels, axles and truck frames showed the need for a more detailed inspection. Also, electrical equipment was, for the most part, hidden away in enclosed equipment cases. As it was largely protected from the elements and dirt and dust, it was only inspected and cleaned at 16-day intervals. A detailed examination of wheels and trucks was done at the same time.

The most rapidly wearing parts on the train were the brake blocks and the current collection shoes. These could only be changed while the train was over a pit. It was gradually determined that it was possible to let a train run for three days without the need to examine shoes or blocks daily and this led to a considerable saving in the use of roads in the sheds with pits. By the end of the first world war, train maintenance had evolved into a 3-daily 'exam' and a 3-weekly 'shed day', the latter replacing the 16-daily inspection. For modern rolling stock today, the same system remains but the '3-daily' is now 14-daily and the '3-weekly' is now 15-weekly — a reflection of the progress made in eliminating wearing parts and improving reliability.

The 3-daily examination and 3-weekly inspection programmes assumed that nothing needed doing to the wheels, motors or bogies which required the lifting of the car. Wheels were gauged for wear on shed-day and, if down to the predetermined limits, the car had to go for lifting and wheel changing. For many years, this was only done when necessary. Lifting of cars on a programmed basis only began in the 1950s.

All cars were regularly swept and cleaned. Exterior cleaning was an onerous task, being performed by hand. It included the application of a sort of polish which preserved the paintwork. This cleaning work was very labour intensive, but helped to preserve the original tube cars, in particular, in very good condition because they were not greatly affected by weather conditions. Very little open running was required by the majority of tube cars until after the extensions of the 1930s. Exterior cleaning by mechanically operated drive-through washing plants was introduced on the District in 1928.

The interior of a very crowded Carbody Shop at Ealing Common Works before the opening of Acton. Both District and Piccadilly stock can be seen here. The crowded conditions clearly demonstrate the need for the extra space which was eventually provided by the opening of the new works at Acton. J. Graeme Bruce collection

Ealing Common Workshop, showing the original wheel area subsequently transferred to Acton Works. On the right foreground is the wheel lathe.

Motor cars on the District were originally given general overhauls every 35,000 miles (38,000 miles for trailers), the equivalent of about eight months' running. The overhaul was largely mechanical and did not include repainting. Cars only began to have their first repaint about two years after electrification. Many of the tube cars, which were steel-bodied, as opposed to the wooden bodies of the District cars, never had a repaint. They were revarnished at regular intervals but their original paintwork survived under layers of varnish and protected by polish until they were scrapped in the late 1920s.

All car maintenance work was originally carried out on a line basis. Each line had a depot with a cleaning shed, an inspection shed and a lifting or overhaul shop. As part of the electrification programme the District Railway constructed a new depot and works at a site subsequently called Ealing Common. At the time of its construction it lay between Mill Hill Park (now Acton Town) and Ealing Common stations with rail access provided at both ends. The road access was at the Ealing Common end, which later gave the name to the depot.

The depot was initially used to prepare the new cars for service after delivery from various carbuilders. The main work included the fitting of the electrical equipment and the traction motors, making up the train units from the individual cars and testing the completed trains. The individual vehicles, because of the American influence, were called cars, not carriages, and the traction motors were fitted to trucks, not bogies. This nomenclature subsequently became the standard practice for Underground rolling stock.

The Bakerloo was opened in 1906 with a depot at a very cramped site adjacent to London Road, Lambeth, which gave the depot its name. The site was not far from the southern terminus at Elephant and Castle. The depot was in a cutting so a special inclined ramp was provided from the entrance gate so that cars being delivered could descend to the running track level after their arrival by road. This line originally had no physical connection with any other railway. It got its main line connection at Queens Park in 1915.

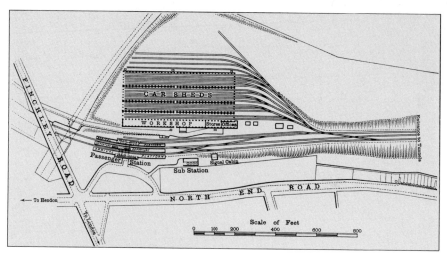

Plan of Golders Green Depot as built. Prior to the opening of Acton Works, this depot was responsible for traction motor repairs.

The Piccadilly, opened in 1906 like the Bakerloo, took over the bulk of the depot site vacated by the District at Lillie Bridge, the District having transferred most of its rolling stock engineering to the new depot at Ealing Common. A new car shed was built on part of the site for the Piccadilly stock and a small shed was provided for the few steam locomotives kept by the District for engineers' trains. The Piccadilly, having a physical connection with the District, had its new cars delivered directly over the railway.

The Hampstead Railway, which was opened in 1907, built almost an identical depot to that at Ealing Common, at least as far as the building formation was concerned. The general layout however was different because Golders Green Depot was single-ended while Ealing Common Depot was double-ended. The Hampstead Railway at this time was also isolated, having no physical connection with any other railway, and its cars were delivered by road from Camden goods yard.

Not all trains were stabled in the main depots at night. On the District in particular, there were various smaller depots where the 3-daily 'exams' could be done. Cromwell Road and East Ham depots were both used for regular exams until the 1950s.

The depots of the District and tube lines tended to share common work. For example, traction motor repairs for all lines were concentrated at Golders Green. Until 1914 there was only one type of traction motor used on the Yerkes tubes, the GE69, a motor which was also used on the District. Ealing Common dealt with wheel, tyre and spring repairs and it had a big wood shop because of the large amount of timber used in District cars. The engineering services for the combine were also located at Ealing, including the administrative and drawing offices.

The three tube lines, the Piccadilly, Bakerloo and Hampstead, although established as separate companies, were amalgamated into one organisation by an Act of Parliament in 1910 as the London Electric Railway Company. This amalgamation took effect from 1st July 1910.

The two other independent tube railways, the City and South London Railway

Truck frames under repair in the original Acton Works in 1924. In the background is a Bakerloo Line gate stock car on its accommodation bogies.

and the Central London Railway, were acquired by the Underground Electric Railways of London Ltd on 1st January 1913 but the advent of the first world war prevented any material changes taking place immediately and the separate rolling stock arrangements continued to function as before.

Both railways had their own major workshops associated with a running depot. The Central London had an extensive self supporting repair depot, including a power station, at Wood Lane, while the City and South London had a works and power station at Stockwell, which was reached from the running tunnels, at first by an incline and later by a hydraulic lift which could take single cars (on this line they were known at this time as carriages).

The Metropolitan Railway, which was not to come under the Underground management until after the formation of London Transport in 1933, had its own extensive works, carriage sidings and power station at Neasden. The works at this location were in fact a very substantial engineering complex employing a large labour force skilled in most of the trades then existing. The Metropolitan Railway had a physical connection with the District Line by virtue of the joint operation of the Circle Line, but the two independent tube railways were isolated and in addition operated under different electric traction collection systems using third rail instead of fourth rail pick-up.

Between 1910 and 1920 the District acquired 200 new cars in addition to its existing stock and the Bakerloo and Piccadilly tubes another 112. Proposals were also afoot for the extension of both the Piccadilly and Hampstead tubes and for the conversion of the C&SLR tunnels to LER standards. Several hundred additional cars would consequently be required and it would be quite beyond the existing capacity of the depots to accommodate and maintain them all. If all these plans were to be implemented extra workshop space would have to be found.

In the meantime, the expansion of the District fleet and the need to rebuild large numbers of the older District cars because of the rapidly deteriorating bodywork, had led to the idea of concentrating car overhauls on a central overhaul site. The policy of centralising overhauls was decided upon in December 1920 and, from this proposal, Acton Works was born.

THE FIRST ACTON WORKS

The new policy to centralise vehicle overhaul for the Underground railways was preceded by a similar policy for the bus part of the organisation. The London General Omnibus Company was also owned by the Underground Group at this time and, in 1919, it was decided that road vehicles should have a central overhaul works. A large area of market gardens on the south side of the District Railway between Acton Town and Chiswick Park was therefore chosen as the site for both bus and rail overhaul shops. The site was divided by the North and South Western Junction Railway and the bus overhaul shops was built on the eastern side of it and named Chiswick Works, while the rail shops were built on the western side and named Acton Works. The only physical connection between the two was a small level crossing over the railway, later replaced by a bridge.

From the beginning of the planning of Acton Works it had been envisaged that it would be built in stages and expanded as necessary. The site which had been acquired made ample provision for this, although a large portion of the ground was allocated on favourable terms to the Metropolitan District Athletic Association, which naturally included the rights of re-entry. A large portion of the ground is still occupied by this Staff Association.

Work began on the detailed design of Acton Works in February 1921 and construction began in the December of that year. During the planning stage, consideration was given to various factory and maintenance systems in use at that time and it was decided to introduce a 'spot system' in the car body shop, whereby each car would remain in the same place while it was worked on. In the truck shop, there was to be a partial progression system, repair to unit parts being concentrated in fitting, smiths and machine shops. It was intended that the progression system would be applied to the whole works eventually.

The plan for the works envisaged the introduction of the facilities in two stages. The first was to include facilities to overhaul the stock of the District, Piccadilly and Bakerloo Lines, about 950 cars. The cost was to be £170,000 including £24,000 for the land. The second 'to be proceeded with later' as a report of November 1922 stated, was to allow the overhaul of the Hampstead, Central London and C&SLR stocks. The second stage was to be twice as large as the first.

The first stage consisted of a large rectangular workshop 400 feet long by 250 feet wide. It was divided into two main areas, one containing the wheel, machining and electrical shops for overhauling the train equipment and mechanical parts, the other, wide enough for five parallel tracks, containing the car body and truck overhaul areas. At each end of the shop, a traverser was provided to allow cars to be moved sideways from one track to another.

Upper Left **A general view of the original Acton Works site in 1924. A 3-car District train is in the centre with the Goliath crane over the wheel storage area on the left. The view is taken from the Acton Town station end of the works. Plenty of spare land has been reserved for future expansion.** U1701

Left **The Acton Works yard with Goliath crane in 1924. The main shop is on the right and, in the background, the Chiswick bus overhaul works can be seen. The North and South Western Junction Railway runs between the two works.**

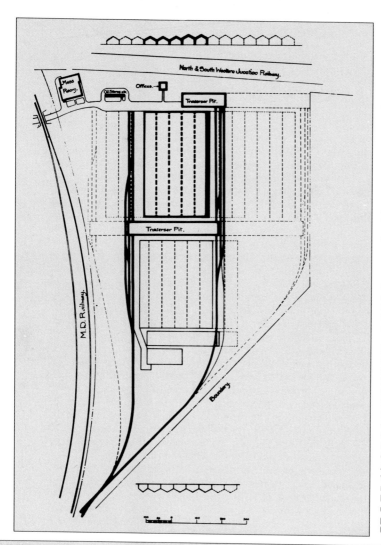

Within the plan:
North & South Western Junction Railway.
Mess Room
Offices
Traverser Pit.
Traverser Pit.
M.D. Railway.
Boundary

A sketch plan drawn by District Railway engineers of the original Acton Works built near Acton Town on the south side of the Metropolitan District Railway line to Ealing. The plan shows in heavy outline the works as opened in 1922 with dotted lines showing the expansions planned for the future. U1702

Below **A District Railway B Stock** motor car on accommodation bogies resting on the No.2 traverser at Acton Works in 1924. The car has been into the dismantling area and is now ready to pass into the main workshop. The car is in remarkably good condition, having already been repainted. In the early days of Acton Works, cars were not repainted there but at depots under a separate programme. U1713

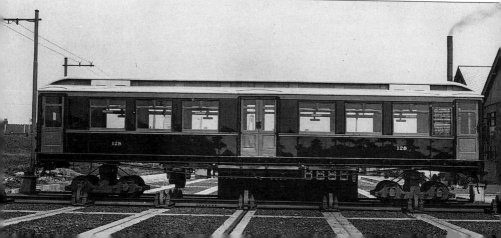

A District D Stock motor car of 1911 vintage over the dismantling pit, being lifted. Its road bogies are about to be rolled forward to the truck dismantling area while the accommodation bogies wait behind to be rolled under the car. Behind is a motor car of F Stock awaiting lifting. U1362

The first cars were overhauled at Acton in December 1922. Each car entered the main shop dismantling area from No.2 traverser. There it was lifted and its bogies moved forward to the truck overhaul area. The body was placed on accommodation bogies and the car transferred via the traverser to the three-road body overhaul area. The accommodation bogies were old Central London trailer bogies which had been replaced by a new design. They were modified to raise the car bodies of vehicles on overhaul so that workers could get underneath without the need for pits.

The three roads in the carbody overhaul area could each take seven cars. One road was reserved for trailers and two for motor cars, the motor cars needing six days for overhaul and the trailers only four days. The production rate began at 16 cars a week, by which time the overhaul mileage had been extended to 60,000 for motor cars and 75,000 for trailers. This was about 14 months' and 18 months' running respectively.

Cars were moved through the shop by electric capstans and equipment removed in the dismantling area was passed through the equipment overhaul shops. The cars and their parts met again at the other end of the carbody shop where there was an assembly area. At first, there was only enough capacity to handle cars

The original truck area of the Works. At the far end of the shop the cars were lifted and the bogies rolled forward to their dismantling area. They were stripped and the frames parked alongside the track, while the parts were moved into the shops on the right hand side for overhaul. Re-assembly took place at the near end of the shop and the finished bogies placed under the car in the 'assembly' area. Car bodies were dealt with on the adjacent three roads as shown here. U1652

A rare photograph of the assembly pits in the original Works in 1924. The car being lifted is A Stock car No. 4 and behind it is a driving trailer of the same stock, No. 304. These two cars were from the batch of 14 cars built for the experimental electrification of the Ealing and South Harrow Railway in 1903. The driving end of No. 4 has been modified to the District standard of the time and the luggage compartment has been converted to first class accommodation. Outside, a gate stock car of 1906 vintage can be seen on the traverser. U1725

from the District and Bakerloo. Although it had been envisaged that Stage I of the works would handle 30 cars per week and Stage II 60 cars per week, it soon became obvious that this was never going to be achieved. The progress of the cars through the shop was slower than anticipated. Cars were often found to get hampered at the testing and assembly end of the sequence, particularly if a previously unnoticed defect was encountered.

In order to meet the planned overhaul of the Piccadilly stock under Stage I, it was found necessary to make a small addition to the works. In 1923 a new and completely separate finishing and inspection shop was provided on the eastern side of the eastern (No 1) traverser where cars passed through for the fitting of shoegear and final checking after overhaul. Once this shop was completed, the production rate went up to 21 cars a week.

The first stock to pass through the works was the District's A Stock, dating from 1903. This had been introduced for the experimental electrification of the Ealing and South Harrow line and originally consisted of fourteen cars. The 1920 District Stock, later known as the F Stock, also had its first overhaul at Acton during 1923. The interiors were refinished to replace the cold styling, the leather upholstery replaced by moquette, and the trucks were modified with stiffer springing. Later in the same year the first tube cars from the Piccadilly Line began passing through the works. The first Bakerloo cars went there in 1924.

Piccadilly Line gate stock trailer car No.251 being lowered onto its bogies in the car assembly area of the original works in February 1924. U2429

Acton Works from the air in 1924. On the right of the main buildings is the yard with the Goliath crane. The two taller buildings are where cars passed through the works. The limits to which the site was eventually expanded can be seen from the position of the dark line in the background. 22289

Acton only began painting cars in 1928. Here, Standard tube and District cars can be seen in the 1928-built Paint Shop. The groove for the chain drive used to move the cars can be seen between the running rails. Even the staging used by the painters for access to the car ends was attached to the chain. U13874

THE FIRST EXTENSION, 1928

Once the production system had settled down at Acton Works following the completion of the inspection and finishing shop, work began on Stage II. This would allow all Underground rolling stock to be overhauled on the site. The Hampstead, C&SLR and Central London stocks were not originally included in the fleet dealt with by Acton, principally because of the difficulty of rail access but, once it was provided, work began on expanding the works to take the stock from these lines.

After the City and South London Railway had come under the control of the Underground group in 1913, plans were formulated for converting the railway and its tunnels to Underground tube standards and for joining it to the Hampstead line at Camden Town. In addition, the Hampstead was to be extended from Golders Green to Edgware. New rolling stock was ordered to provide the additional services and to replace the loco-hauled stock of the City and South London. Powers were also obtained in 1923 for an extension at the southern end of the Hampstead from Charing Cross to Kennington to make another junction with the C&SLR and to extend that line from Clapham to Morden. By the time the last of these additions was finally brought into service on 13th September 1926, the rolling stock fleet of the combined line, now known as the Hampstead and City, had risen to 726 cars from the total of approximately 350 vehicles which operated on the two original lines.

Included in the Hampstead and City scheme was the provision of a physical connection between the Hampstead and City and the Piccadilly Line at Kings Cross to enable stock transfers to be made to and from Acton Works. Until the connection was brought into operational use on 27th March 1927, all stock movements to and from Golders Green Depot, and the new depot built at Morden, had to be undertaken by road. The new cars were all delivered by road but it was not intended to make such moves by road to meet overhaul requirements at Acton Works.

Rebuilding work to increase the capacity at Acton Works started in 1925 and was not totally completed until 1928. Hampstead and City rolling stock had, by then, begun to be overhauled at Acton and now represented a larger block of cars than the District fleet.

After the extension of the Central London Railway service over tracks provided by the Great Western Railway from Wood Lane to Ealing Broadway on 3rd August 1920, it became possible to provide a physical connection with the District and so enable direct communication with Acton Works. However, there was still a problem because the Central London Railway operated with a current rail collection system different from the other railways in the Underground group, as it used a central positive rail with the running rail return.

The standard Underground four rail system was first established for the original South Harrow electrification of the District Railway in 1903. It had the positive rail outside the running rails and a centre negative rail, providing an insulated system which continues to be used on the Underground today. The 3-rail Central London cars could not therefore be transferred to and from Acton

F Stock and B Stock cars awaiting removal from the exit roads of the original Works in 1924. During the 1928 expansion of the works, the new carbody shop was built over these tracks. U1680

Works under their own power, so transfers from Ealing Broadway were carried out by steam locomotive. The cars were usually placed between match wagons which were provided with the Central London bar and link at one end and what was at that time called the RCH (for Railway Clearing House) coupling at the other end for attaching to a steam locomotive or brake van. In fact, the rakes were usually formed between two brake vans because the locomotive was required to run round the train at Ealing Broadway in both directions. This arrangement continued until 1940 when the Central London Railway was converted to the Underground standard. It was then possible for trains to and from Acton Works to be transferred under their own power. When Central London rolling stock overhaul was transferred to Acton in 1928, another 259 cars were added to the fleet in the overhaul cycle.

Before beginning overhauls at Acton, the Central London stock was converted from having gated passenger entrances at the car ends to having enclosed ends and air operated sliding doors. The work was carried out between 1926 and 1928 at the Underground-owned Union Construction Company works at Feltham and it was planned that subsequent overhauls would begin at Acton in 1928. Prior to this, the trucks of the cars undergoing conversion were overhauled at Acton and, when the bodies returned from Feltham, they were sent to Acton by road to be reunited with their trucks before transfer by rail to Wood Lane and final pre-service finishing.

With the addition of the C&SLR and CLR fleets, the total stock now being serviced at Acton Works was 2,090 cars, of which some 1,406 had to pass through the works each year. This meant that the Works' output had to be of the order of 30 cars per week. It is interesting to note that this was the originally planned output of the Stage I workshops but it was not achieved until Stage II was completed.

Following the successful operation of the scheme introduced at Chiswick Works for bus overhaul, the extension to Acton was planned so that cars would be overhauled on the progression or flow-line principle. Cars would pass through the workshops while work was performed on them at various stopping places on the way. It was based on the modern manufacturing techniques then being introduced in the motor industry. With this system, Acton Works became one of the most modern railway overhaul shops in the world, a position which it was to hold for over 30 years.

The introduction of the flow-line principle meant a complete reorganisation of the Works, involving construction of the new shops completed in 1928. The enlarged Works now consisted of five main shops. The Truck Shop, the Body Shop and the Paint Shop were contained in the main building, which now measured some 400 feet by 375 feet with seven bays in the 375ft width, two more than before, while a new Lifting Shop and Wood Shop were provided in separate buildings.

The 1928 expansion of the works saw the introduction of the 'blow out shop'. Accumulated dust and dirt was removed from underneath the car body. The cleaning was completed by a combination of compressed air jets directed by hand held lances and general suction ducts. On the lower right can be seen the 'dog' mounted on the haulage chain which was attached to the accommodation bogie to move the car body. U4769

The new Lifting Shop was arranged to be at the beginning and the end of the overhaul cycle and it included a 50ton duplex overhead crane which dealt with both incoming and outgoing cars. This crane had a 65ft span with two lifting dogs which could be used singly or jointly to lift a whole car body and traverse it across the whole width of the shop above other cars standing on their bogies.

The Lifting Shop was divided into four sections. The incoming section received the cars from the reception road, transferred them to accommodation bogies, then passed the carbody into a blow-out enclosure for the removal of encrusted dust and dirt before they were put onto the traverser for conveyance to the bodyshop. Meanwhile the trucks belonging to the car were passed directly to the Truck Shop.

The outgoing section, also covered by the same duplex crane, received the completed cars and trucks and remarried them before passing them out to sidings, where they would await train make-up and despatch to the appropriate depots.

A general repair section, which occupied two of the tracks served by the duplex crane, was used to accommodate cars requiring heavy repairs or modifications outside the overhaul cycle. These heavy repairs were those outside the capacity of the normal overhaul shops, involving repairs after electrical fires or fusings, installation of new equipment such as heaters, or the turning of cars — so that west end cars could become east end cars or vice versa — which required wiring and coupling position alterations.

The need to turn cars began on the District in 1927. The District stock formations required some additional east end motor cars and a turning programme at Acton was arranged. Turning of cars became a regular job at Acton both for the tube and surface lines and has continued ever since.

At this time cars which ran on the Piccadilly, Hampstead, Central or Bakerloo tunnel sections were not fitted with heaters. It was found however that heaters were required for the winter on those cars working between Golders Green and Edgware and on the Central London between Wood Lane and Ealing Broadway and, later, on the Piccadilly extensions opened in the early 1930s. Acton became involved in several programmes for the fitting of heaters during this period.

The fourth section of the Lifting Shop was situated between the incoming and outgoing sections and dealt with seats. It received the seats taken out of the cars as they were dealt with on the dismantling road. It became known as the trimming area. Seats were cleaned, repaired and stored in this section whilst awaiting replacement in overhauled car bodies. Space was required for about 40 car sets of seats since the cars themselves were now in the works on average about 10 working days. The increase over the original 4-6 days was largely due to the fact that painting was now part of the overhaul cycle.

Following the dismounting of car bodies from their trucks at the reception road of the Lifting Shop, the trucks passed into the rearranged Truck Shop where the traction motors continued to be removed as the first step in the complete stripping of the bogies. Wherever possible, conveyors were installed to reduce the manhandling of heavy components. The Truck Shop itself consisted of five main parts and was equipped with two electrically operated conveyors, one for dismantling and the other for assembly of the trucks. These conveyors travelled at about seven inches per minute in opposite directions, with the dismantling conveyor on the inward side of the shop and the assembling conveyor on the other side. The sections of the shop were placed between these conveyors and, where necessary, cross shop conveyors or transporters were arranged to move the materials from the dismantling conveyor through the appropriate repair sections of the shop to the assembly conveyor.

Standard Stock from the Northern Line arriving at the entrance to the lifting shop at the start of its overhaul cycle in July 1933. The trailer car is uncoupled and then moved into the lifting shop. U12546

A 1925 Standard Stock motor car being lifted off its bogies on the entrance road of the lifting shop in June 1934. The leading motor bogie has larger wheels than the trailer bogie and the floor of the car had to be raised over it to give the necessary clearance. This was a feature of tube car design until the arrival of the 1935 and subsequent stocks which all had flat floors throughout. U14656

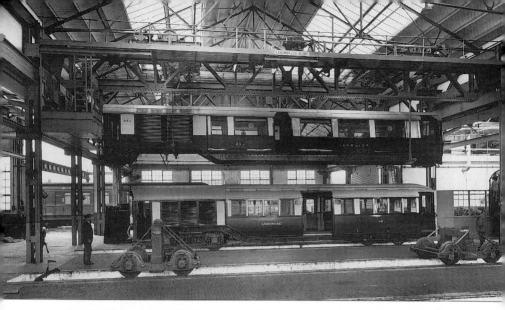

Two cars of tube stock in the Lifting Shop shortly after it was commissioned in 1928. The car in the air is 1920 Watford Joint Stock motor car No.25J, whilst underneath is 1915 Ealing Stock motor car No.401 from the Central London Line. The Watford car had inward opening swing doors whilst the Ealing car, which originally had them too, was rebuilt to have air doors in 1927. Note the differing heights of the accommodation bogies required to carry the two-level floors of the tube motor cars. U4760

The Watford car has been lowered onto its road bogies and will now be tested prior to its return to service. U4758

An electric truck as used in the early days of the Works for carrying traction motors and similar equipment. The original machines were provided by Ransomes and, from that time, all electric trucks of similar type used at Acton were called Ransomes, irrespective of manufacturer. U1715

The Motor Shop was in this area. A special armature transporter was provided which ran across the Motor Shop with a maximum speed of 5mph. There were also small cranes to help in the dismantling and repair of traction motors. A special adjacent, but segregated, shop, which at this time was entirely manned by female staff, was provided for manufacturing and insulating armature bars and rewinding small wire wound coils. This type of work was traditionally one where women operatives were employed, in those days of course on a lower pay scale.

The suspension and brake gear section in the Truck Shop dealt with all the pieces easily removable from the bogies during dismantling and it contained a blacksmiths and springsmiths section. At this time all the cars were braked by means of a single brake cylinder carried under the carbody which applied the individual brake blocks on the wheels by means of brake rigging. As already mentioned all of these parts were not only prone to wear but often developed fatigue cracks. The main suspension system, which was by means of wagon type plate springs and steel coil springs, was also subject to wear and fatigue cracks and it also underwent careful examination and repair.

After the removal of all its individual pieces the truck frame was lifted off its wheels and placed on a cross shop conveyor which moved at a speed of 4½ inches per minute. Unless work of an exceptional character was found, the examination and normal repair of truck frames was carried out on this conveyor. When the frame reached the end of the conveyor it was placed on the assembly conveyor and built up for return to its carbody. The work carried out in the truck frame section consisted of riveting, welding and replacing of parts, including the axle box guides. The original motor bogies were made of cast steel but those built immediately before the first world war were of pressed steel, while later ones were constructed of riveted plate and angle.

The final part of the dismantling process in the truck shop was when the axle boxes themselves were removed from the wheels. The weight of axleboxes necessitated the provision of a sloping conveyor so that little manhandling was necessary to get them through the washing plant provided for degreasing before their distribution into the shop. At this time, all the axle bearings were of white metal, including the armature bearings and the motor suspension bearings, but, in the late 1920s, plans were being formulated for the conversion of the armature bearings to the ball and roller type. The more modern motors, such as the WT54, GE260, GE212 and MV552 types, were converted to this arrangement between 1928 and 1933 and special equipment was installed in the works to deal with this task. These motors however continued to use white metal suspension bearings on the axles until the end of their lives.

The wheels left on the dismantling conveyor were tested for flaws in the axles on a magnetic testing device. At this time, one of the most serious maintenance problems was the detection of fatigue cracks in axles to reduce the risk of them breaking in passenger service. The only means of flaw detection possible at the time was by the magnetic crack method. A magnetising device had end clamps which were pressed onto the end of the axle. Powdered iron mixed in paraffin was then poured over the axle. Should an axle have a crack developing, the magnetic flux caused the powdered iron to adhere to the sides of the crack and form a black line.

The magnetic testing device could locate the formation of an incipient crack only on the exposed parts of an individual axle. This excluded the areas of the wheel and gear seats, which could not therefore be tested. This was a problem not solved until the introduction of ultrasonic testing after the second world war.

Left **Broken axles were much more common in the early years of this century than they are today. The risks and disruptions caused by a breakage while a train was in service led to detection systems for craked axles being installed. Shown here is a magnetic axle crack detector.**
J. Graeme Bruce collection

Below **A more modern system for crack detection known as ultrasonic testing was introduced after the second world war. Here, the operator of the system is seen observing the shape of a signal on the monitor screen. The shape of the signal indicated the existence, or not, of a crack or potential failure of the axle.** U38565

Another regular system of testing was carried out on axles, known as the tup test. This was a destructive test which consisted of dropping a heavy weight on the supported axle under test, which would then either bend or fracture. The resultant metallurgical examination of the sample cut from the axle determined whether the remainder of the cast from which the sample came should continue to run in service or should be withdrawn and scrapped.

The application of the tup test required an accurate recording system to be developed, not only for the metallurgical records of the casts used in the manufacture of the axles but also for the location of all the axles of a particular cast. A system of controlling withdrawals from service following an adverse report, or of obtaining a sample for test due to the passage of time, as well as the accumulation of critical mileage, had also to be arranged. This job would today be simply controlled by a computer but, at that time, required a large records office containing a considerable amount of detail and cross referencing of information. The development of such a system created a large amount of work not only in accurate recording of all the information concerning axles but in the replacement of those axles removed from service arising from the testing and condemnation system.

When a cast of axles exceeded 500,000 miles, 2% of the cast was withdrawn and subjected to technical tests laid down in British Standard Specifications. The tup testing plant had originally been installed in connection with these tests. Should the selected axles fail to meet the requirements of the tests, the whole cast was condemned, otherwise the process was repeated at each succeeding 150,000 miles until 1,000,000 miles was reached, which was considered to be the maximum safe life in passenger service.

Axles were scrapped after a fixed life or upon detection of a crack. Wheels and gears had to be removed. Here a duplex wheel and gear press is seen in the enlarged wheel area of Acton Works. J. Graeme Bruce collection

A traction motor being removed from its bogie in the special area reserved for this operation in the lifting shop. The bogies would then be drawn forward to the truck shop on the other side of No.2 Traverser for overhaul. In the lifting area behind is a Standard Stock control trailer awaiting removal from its bogies. U30409

Following considerable experience of the magnetic test system it became evident that most of the faults which did eventually cause the axles to fracture later in their life occurred inside the wheel seats. These could not be detected directly by the magnetic crack detector unless the wheels were pressed off the axles so that the whole surface was visible, an expensive operation to do on a regular basis. Efforts were therefore made to develop a type of non-destructive testing which could cover the whole axle without dismantling. Eventually ultrasonic testing, a new technique developed after the end of the second world war, provided the answer and, subsequently, magnetic testing was only used to confirm the existence of a crack in a dismantled axle which had been found suspect by the ultrasonic test.

A major advantage of the ultrasonic axle testing system was that it could be carried out whilst the axle was under the car and therefore could be done at depots at any convenient time. All axles were henceforth designed with journals having plain polished ends so that the ultrasonic probes could be manipulated freely around the full face of the journal. The ultrasonic testing equipment required an experienced operator and to encourage the accurate detection of defective axles an award was paid for the location of a crack in the axle.

As the operators became more expert in dealing with the equipment, this arrangement resulted in many suspect axles being found. The depth of the crack became important and the award was thus split to cover a payment when the incipient crack was first discovered, the remainder being paid when the crack required the axle to be withdrawn. By this means axles were not removed unnecessarily but it did mean that the regular testing schedules had to be maintained.

The pairs of wheels, or wheelsets, themselves required a lot of attention including turning, renewal of tyres, and occasional removal and replacement of axles as well as of the gear wheels fitted on motor axles. Equipment was provided for all these processes. Wheels were also sent from the depots to Acton for reprofiling as the machines then installed at Acton were the most modern.

All wheels on Underground rolling stock at that time were of the tyred type, that is generally having a spoked cast centre onto which a steel tyre was shrunk, and which was then either riveted in position in the case of the early motor wheels or, on later wheels, was held by a retaining ring which was rolled into a groove to make the tyre secure.

The original wheel lathe installed in the Works. Wheels had to be reprofiled when worn to ensure stability and safety when running. Successive sessions on the wheel lathe could reduce the wheel diameter from new by 1¾ inches before the tyre had to be scrapped U1690

Machines had to be provided both to remove rivets and to cut out the retaining rings to enable old tyres to be removed. The tyres were then cut by an oxy-acetylene blow torch, after which they could easily be removed by a special tyre removing machine leaving the wheel centre clear for the fitting of a replacement tyre. This process only took place when the wheel diameter had reached the scrapping stage. A 36inch diameter motor wheel, for example, required tyre renewal when it had been reduced to 32½ inches. This would take an average of about four years. Trailer wheel tyres took somewhat longer to reduce to the scrapping size.

Movement of the car bodies on their accommodation bogies between shops was carried out by the 45ton traversers. The original two machines provided at each end of the main shop had their tracks extended to cover the 1928 expansion of the works. No.2 traverser moved incoming cars from the Blowout Shop to the Carbody Shop, from the Carbody Shop to an outside 'chain' road used to get cars from the main shop to the Paint Shop, and from the Paint Shop back to the outgoing section of the Lifting Shop. No.1 traverser moved the cars from the incoming Carbody Shop road to the outgoing road and from the outside chain road to the Paint Shop. It could also move cars into the roads provided in the Wood Shop. The traversers themselves were fitted with electric haulage winches which could move the car bodies with their accommodation bogies on or off the appropriate haulage chains.

Left **Tyre removing machine, as used in the 1930s and subsequently. The tyre was cut with an acetylene torch and then pulled off the wheel centre as shown in the foreground.** Right **Tyres were held on the wheel by a retaining ring or by riveting. Here, the retaining ring is being rolled onto the back of the tyre to make it secure. These rings were removed by a simple lathe which turned out the rollover of the ring.** J. Graeme Bruce collection

New tyres were fitted by heating them and then shrinking them onto the wheel centre. An electric induction heater was used at Acton to heat the tyres as seen here. A District F Stock car can be seen on the dismantling road in the background. U1684

Motor tyres were riveted onto the wheels for additional safety. Special rivet removal machines were provided as were riveting machines like this one. Today, wheels and tyres are no longer separate. The whole wheel is cast in a single bloom and rolled to become what is known as a monobloc wheel.

District E Stock car 276 on the No. 1 traverser at Acton, having been restored to its road bogies and ready to move to the exit roads behind the camera. Note that the underframe equipment and bogies have been overhauled but the body has not been painted. Painting was not done at Acton until 1928. U1718

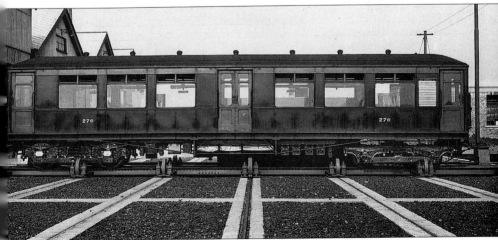

Acton Works from the air after the 1928 extensions had been built. Their clean roofs distinguish them from the 1922 buildings. Nearest the camera is the new Wood Shop; behind the sidings is the three-road Paint Shop and the two-road Carbody Shop. The other new building is the Lifting Shop. 23639

With the 1928 extensions the Carbody Shop was arranged so that the cars passed up one side while the equipment was dismantled and down the other side while it was replaced. The dismantling road was equipped with an electrically driven chain moving at 10 inches per minute. The accommodation bogies were attached to the chain by means of dogs locking on to the chain. The assembly road was in the form of a conveyor, both its tracks and the floor between the tracks moving at a speed of 10 inches per minute, an arrangement which ensured that equipment could be easily refitted because assembly was much more difficult and time consuming than dismantling. The speeds of the chain and the conveyor ensured that the cars were in the Carbody Shop about three working days.

As part of the 1928 expansion of the works, the repainting of the car bodies was tied into the overhaul cycle and so a new Paint Shop was provided. It was equipped with three tracks, each provided with an electrically driven endless chain. Two of the roads were used for what was referred to as touching up and revarnishing and was carried out under movement with the speed of the chains arranged at three inches per minute. The more modern tube cars, particularly those doing most of their running in tunnels and requiring only cleaning and one paint coat plus revarnishing, took about three days on these tracks. The third road was set apart for stripping and full repainting. The chain on this road could be operated at a fast speed so that the movement was intermittent from position to position as finished cars were cleared off the end position. Each track held a maximum of seven cars when fully loaded.

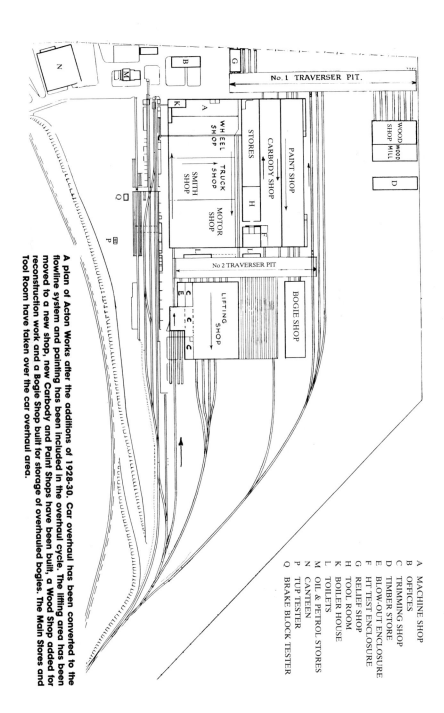

A plan of Acton Works after the additions of 1928-30. Car overhaul has been converted to the flowline system and painting has been included in the overhaul cycle. The lifting area has been moved to a new shop, new Carbody and Paint Shops have been built, a Wood Shop added for reconstruction work and a Bogie Shop built for storage of overhauled bogies. The Main Stores and Tool Room have taken over the car overhaul area.

No. 1 TRAVERSER PIT.

WOOD SHOP MILL

No 2 TRAVERSER PIT

WHEEL SHOP

TRUCK SHOP

SMITH SHOP

MOTOR SHOP

STORES

CARBODY SHOP

PAINT SHOP

BOGIE SHOP

LIFTING SHOP

A   MACHINE SHOP
B   OFFICES
C   TRIMMING SHOP
D   TIMBER STORE
E   BLOW-OUT ENCLOSURE
F   HT TEST ENCLOSURE
G   RELIEF SHOP
H   TOOL ROOM
K   BOILER HOUSE
L   TOILETS
M   OIL & PETROL STORES
N   CANTEEN
P   TUP TESTER
Q   BRAKE BLOCK TESTER

The Paint Shop flow-line worked from what became known as the Acton End of the shop towards the Ealing End. These descriptions were used for many years for all the shops in the works although they had little reference to geographical fact. The Acton End of the works faced Chiswick and the Ealing End faced Acton Town station. The nomenclature seems to have been a legacy of the days when the works was based at Ealing Common.

After leaving the Ealing End of the Carbody Shop, the car bodies had to be traversed to the outside chain road to convey them to the Acton End for movement into the Paint Shop. This chain road was under the control of the traverser operators and movement could be made in either direction because it was also required to feed cars to and from the Wood Shop as well as to the Paint Shop. The operating chain was only in movement when a car had been placed on it. Its speed was 30 inches per minute.

The Wood Shop was equipped with an up to date wood mill providing new parts for all sections of the works and for the depots. Standing accommodation was provided for seven cars in the shop to allow heavy repairs to those car bodies which required them to be stationary for fairly long periods. Work on floors, ceilings and body frames, plus collision damage repairs, was undertaken in this area.

The arrangement of the workshops at Acton at this time was the first installation in the world where railway rolling stock was completely overhauled on a continuously moving system. The arrangements were made possible by the similarity of equipment throughout the fleet but, even so, differences in work load occurred between motor cars, control trailers and trailers and a balance of the different types had to be carefully planned to ensure that the work was properly distributed throughout the complex.

Another aspect of planning at Acton was that truck overhaul took a lot less time than car body overhaul. Completed trucks were therefore stored for several days waiting for their car bodies before remounting in the Lifting Shop. A special three road shop was built opposite the Ealing End of the Paint Shop to accommodate completed trucks. It appears to have been built after the 1928 extensions were completed and it was certainly in use by 1931. It had a 15ton overhead crane to allow trucks to be picked out and sent to the Lifting Shop when required for placing under completed car bodies.

The staff in the works had now been increased to some 900 personnel from the 500 employed in 1924 and general overhauls at running depots ceased altogether. It had now become the general practice to use road transport to interchange components requiring heavy repairs on a one for one basis between the depots and Acton Works. Such items as pairs of wheels, traction motors and compressors were dealt with in this way as well as renewable items such as white metal bearings and leaf springs which were also renovated and repaired at Acton.

By the time the LER tube lines had all been equipped with new air door stock (the Standard Tube Stock) in 1930, and the extensions to Acton Works were complete, the overhaul mileages had been extended. All Standard Stock cars were overhauled at 100,000 miles (roughly two years' running), while Central London motor cars went to Acton at 60,000 miles (70,000 miles for trailers) and District motor cars at 80,000 miles (90,000 miles for trailers). By that time, Acton had to deal with about 2400 cars, an increase of 300 over the 1928 total, but the Works was still dealing with about 30 each week.

Trains of tube and District stock ready for return to service after overhaul at Acton in July 1933. On the left is a train of Central London stock dating from 1903. This stock was originally gated but was converted to air doors in 1927-8 at Feltham. This particular train has been converted for use on the Ealing service. Note the right-hand driving position. Left-hand driving was normal on the Underground but some Central London cars had right hand drive. U12586

The interior of the Paint Shop in July 1933 with a District C Stock motor car being painted on the left and a Standard Stock trailer on the right. U12547

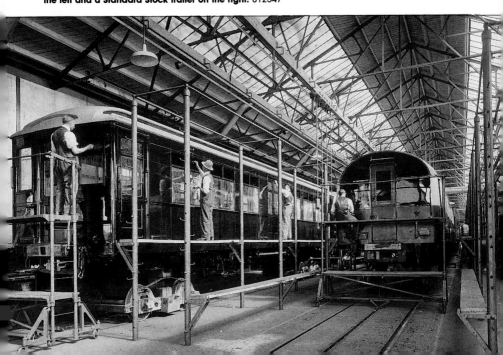

Top **The Metropolitan Railway Works at Neasden from the air. From 1934, overhaul work for Metropolitan stock was gradually taken over by Acton, and Neasden was rebuilt to become a running depot for the Metropolitan and Bakerloo Lines.** H7227

Above **The interior of the car shed at the original Neasden Works in 1935 showing Metropolitan Railway compartment and saloon stock. In the foreground is a 1931-built motor coach of what was to become known as T Stock.** U19625

THE METROPOLITAN INFLUENCE

The London Passenger Transport Board was formed in 1933 to take over the operation of bus and underground rail services in London. As far as the Underground was concerned, this involved little change in day to day operations except that the hitherto independent Metropolitan Railway became part of the Underground organisation. For Acton Works, another expansion programme was going to be needed to absorb the Metropolitan's rolling stock into the overhaul process.

The Metropolitan's first rolling stock workshop was at Edgware Road but, as the railway expanded, the premises became too small and, in 1880, it was decided to build a new carriage and locomotive repair works on land acquired adjacent to the river Brent at Neasden. In 1904, for electrification, a power station was built next to the works site as well as a repair and running shed for the electric rolling stock. By 1909, almost 900 staff were employed at Neasden, of whom less than 100 were concerned with the power station. By 1933, this workforce had reached close to 1,000 persons.

In order to provide accommodation for the staff, the Metropolitan built a number of cottages to the north of the site. They became known as Neasden Village. The properties came into the ownership of London Transport where they remained until recent years.

There was considerable diversity of services offered by the Metropolitan. Not only were freight and passenger services provided but these were both steam and electric operated and they covered the heavily used underground routes as well as suburban and longer distance journeys to the north west of London.

The rolling stock was just as diverse. Both saloon stock with sliding doors and compartment stock of the traditional British variety was used in multiple unit trains, often mixing the two types in the same train. Electric and steam locomotives as well as multiple unit and hauled passenger stock were based at Neasden and the workshops there handled all the different types of stock.

The Metropolitan's rolling stock policy had been somewhat inconsistent over the years. Not only were trains purchased with incompatible electrical equipment but also with incompatible braking systems and incompatible couplers. Some trains had vacuum brakes, like many of the main line railways at the time, while others had Westinghouse air brakes as used by the Underground group and generally preferred by most railways for electric multiple unit stock. Electrical equipment came from British Westinghouse (later Metropolitan Vickers), British Thompson-Houston and the General Electric Company. As for the couplings, some trains used the RCH buffer and screw coupling system, some had plain links within train sets, and some used the Buckeye automatic mechanical coupler pioneered in America, a modern version of which is now standard for Underground engineers' vehicles.

When the Metropolitan was taken over by London Transport, it had a total of eleven different types of train operating over its tracks. The new organisation quickly decided to reduce these to as few as possible, eventually getting down to five basic types. Most of the work to make this possible was undertaken at Neasden but using support from Acton as required.

One of the first rationalisation schemes for the Metropolitan's stock concerned the Circle Line service. Eighteen 5-car trains were made up from saloon stock, most of which was built between 1912 and 1921, to provide the daily service of fourteen trains for the Circle and give four spare trains for maintenance.

The trains were completely renovated at Neasden. They were formed into five trains with BT-H equipment and thirteen with British Westinghouse equipment. All the cars had end communicating doors added, unless already provided, in accordance with standard Underground practice. By the time the twelfth train was in work, late in 1934, it had been decided to remove the luggage compartments on the motor cars and provide a small guard's compartment in its place. The remaining trains were modified in this way as they were renovated. Earlier trains were modified at Acton Works when they were sent there for their next overhaul, beginning in 1936.

As part of their renovation at Neasden, the Circle trains were repainted in the Underground colours of red bodywork and cream upper panels. During the late 1930s, this became all red because of the difficulty of keeping the cream panels clean. The interiors of the cars were repainted cerulean blue and cream.

The bulk of the remaining Metropolitan saloon stock dated from the 1904-7 period of the original electrification scheme and it was due for replacement by the time London Transport took it over. This began in 1937 with the introduction of the new O Stock, the first batch of Metadyne equipped stock. As a result, very few of the old saloon stock vehicles received an overhaul at Acton. However, after completion of the Circle stock programme, many of the specialist staff at Neasden engaged on carriage work were transferred to Acton.

With the decision to transfer overhauls to Acton, the original works at Neasden became redundant and the whole site was rebuilt as a running depot for the Metropolitan and Bakerloo Lines. A new Bakerloo branch was built in tunnel from a junction at Baker Street with the original line to a junction with the Metropolitan at Finchley Road. Tube trains began working through to Stanmore, taking over what had been the Metropolitan stopping service from 20th November 1939. This service is now part of the Jubilee Line.

The reconstruction of Neasden and the transfer of Metropolitan overhauls to Acton resulted in some significant changes at Acton Works. Apart from the expansion of the works, of which more in the next chapter, Acton saw some changes in its work. The two Pullman cars operated by the Metropolitan were sent to Acton during 1935. They had originally been ordered from W.S. Laycock of Sheffield in 1910 but the building was sub-contracted to the Birmingham Railway Carriage and Wagon Co. Laycock supplied the fittings, equipment, interior decoration and furniture. Public service began on 1st June 1910 and continued until it was abandoned at the outbreak of the second world war in 1939. It was never reinstated.

Other changes at Acton included the importation of additional skills to deal with the influx of compartment stock. There were considerable problems with swing slam doors. Until the last of this type of stock, by then known as T Stock, was phased out in 1962, a major industry for the Acton Wood Shop was the provision of spare swing doors which had to be manufactured in considerable quantities. Doors were frequently damaged entering the tunnel at Finchley Road if they had not been properly closed before the train moved off.

The doors of compartment stock were designed for trains stopping at platforms on the 'nearside', so that they tended to swing closed if the train started with them left open. On the other hand, if leaving an island platform or one on the 'offside', doors tended to fly open and were more prone to damage. The problem

In this view of the Paint Shop in 1951 are cars of P Stock, Standard and 1938 Tube stocks and, on the extreme left, a 1931-built Metropolitan Line T Stock motor coach. Metropolitan stock began to appear at Acton after the takeover of the Metropolitan Railway by the London Passenger Transport Board in 1934. LT32

was particularly acute at Finchley Road southbound, where the trains entered a tunnel with very limited clearance. An 'open door detector' was fitted on the southbound road to try to reduce the number of incidents of door damage but it was never very successful and was later removed.

Acton also saw new painting techniques. Much of the Metropolitan stock had been finished in varnished teak and, even when steel panelled compartment stock was acquired in 1932 (the last batch of T Stock), the wood grain was reproduced to continue the effect. The Paint Shop at Acton took over the work for a while but it was found to be very time consuming and it required skilled craftsmen. At the end of the second world war, shortages of skilled labour forced the abandonment of the grained finish and all the compartment stock was finished in a plain brown or light chocolate colour.

When the Metropolitan first became part of London Transport in 1934, some experimental liveries were tried out on the compartment stock. One coach was painted in an all-red livery and another in red with black lining. Various other shades were tried, including an all-green similar to that used on the Southern Railway. None were generally adopted.

The Metropolitan had four different types of electric train containing compartment stock as well as the locomotive-hauled stock. All had 1927-32 built motor coaches of what became T Stock and these had their luggage compartments reduced and replaced by additional seating at Acton. The trailers were of various types including older 'Ashbury' coaches and saloon cars. These were eventually withdrawn and some were replaced by locomotive-hauled coaches converted by Acton in 1940 to run with the motor coaches.

Technical modifications included the conversion of three vacuum braked trains to the standard Westinghouse air brake and the conversion of the gear ratio of certain GEC equipped motor coaches to make them compatible with the rest of the T Stock. This work was also done at Acton.

A new 6-road paint shop was opened in February 1938 and it is seen here with various stocks undergoing wiring modifications in connection with the fitting of electro-pneumatic brakes and passenger door control. Before it could be commissioned for painting work, it was pressed into service for modification work and then for war work. U26469

NEW WORKS PROGRAMME, 1935-40

A considerable scheme for improving transport facilities in London was agreed in 1934 between the Treasury, the four main line railway companies and the London Passenger Transport Board. It included the building of twelve miles of new tube railway, the electrification of about 44 miles of suburban railways and the doubling of track and electrification of another 12½ miles of railways, over some of which tube services would be operated. The 1935-40 New Works Programme, as these schemes were called, required the provision of new rolling stock to be operated by London Transport.

Before the New Works Programme was begun, the total passenger rolling stock of the Underground was in the region of 3,100 vehicles, including 84 steam hauled coaches. In addition there were 51 electric locomotives, of which 27 were used on passenger trains. To provide cars for new services and to replace those considered to be over age, the Board ordered 1,690 new cars. In all, an increase of roughly 25% in the number of cars was planned.

The start of the second world war in September 1939, when work on the programme was well advanced, led to a gradual run down in the construction of extensions and electrification, largely due to the shortage of staff occasioned by the call to arms. Although most of the rolling stock was delivered, the failure to complete the Central Line extensions to Ruislip, Hainault and Epping meant that large numbers of Standard Stock cars intended for this line were stored for the duration. The extensions were not opened until after the war and the condition of the rolling stock after years of storage was to become a serious problem which was only partly solved by a large scale programme of work by Acton, as will be seen.

The large increase in the fleet and the introduction of new equipment on rolling stock as a result of the New Works Programme meant a further expansion of Acton Works, coupled with technical advances in the workshop equipment. Four new shops were constructed to enlarge the works, together with extensive alterations to the existing shops.

A completely new Machine Shop was constructed at the Acton End of the works, enabling an expansion of the existing Wheel Shop into the area of the original Machine Shop. The main function of the Machine Shop was to manufacture in quantity components such as pins and bushes, which were placed in the stores to be drawn on as required. The machines provided for this work consisted of a complement of automatic and semi-automatic lathes, drills, borers, millers and planers with multi-spindle automatic lathes as well as pre-tooled capstan lathes. In addition, copying lathes for machining axles from roughly forged billets were provided.

The Machine Shop was supported by a well equipped Tool Room supplying jigs and fixtures and which was equipped with case hardening furnaces to improve the wearing properties of steel items.

The Tool Room was built on the site of the original Inspection and Finishing Shop. Following the 1928 reorganisation of the Works, this had become what was called the Relief Shop. It was demolished to allow the Tool Room to be built.

At the same time, the northern end of No. 1 traverser was cut back and replaced by a widened roadway to allow better access to the main store which had taken over the site of the original Carbody Shop.

A new Motor Shop was built at the Ealing End of the Works. The removal of motor overhauls to this new shop released space in the Truck Shop and allowed the truck overhaul process to be rearranged and expanded. The resiting of the Motor Shop away from the progressive sequence of overhaul meant that the process of refitting overhauled motors to overhauled trucks was moved from the Truck Shop to the Lifting Shop. It now took place when the overhauled car bodies arrived to be matched with their trucks. Motor bogies could now be stored outside since they no longer carried their motors and did not now need special protection from the weather.

The new Motor Shop, covering 20,000 square feet, was arranged for the overhaul of all types of electrical machines. The principal facility was, of course, designed to deal with the large number of traction motors, of which there were eventually 6,000 in use on the system.

All traction motors were first placed on stands in a special area and cleaned before dismantling. To facilitate the dismantling, special stands were designed which enabled the motor case to be rotated and locked in any position so that examination and repairs could be carried out at a convenient angle.

Sections of the Motor Shop were designed to deal with motor cases, field coils, frameheads and bearings. The most vulnerable part of an electric motor is the armature and, to deal with them, a well-equipped armature shop was provided. The armature transporter which had been designed for the original Motor Shop was transferred to the new shop. It was similar to one which was used in the Wheel Shop for transporting pairs of wheels across the shop. It ran on a special track and travelled at 5mph.

In the armature section the work moved progressively from stripping to finishing, during which time work such as rewinding, rebanding, vacuum impregnating with insulating varnish and stoving in an oven was carried out. Afterwards, the rebuilt armatures were balanced on a special dynamic balancing machine and given a high tension current insulation test at double the normal traction voltage, i.e. at 1250 volts.

As an adjunct to the new Motor Shop, a new taping room was provided for the forming and insulation of armature bars. Many other electrical coils were also produced there as required. As with the original taping room, all the staff were female.

A new Trimming Shop was also built at this time on the Ealing side of the new Motor Shop. This allowed the Lifting Shop, which had contained the trimming area, to receive a second blow-out facility for the cleaning of incoming cars. There was originally space for only one car and this was now expanded to two.

There was considerable variation in the cleaning time for different types of cars because the levels of dirt accumulated varied according to the line on which the car operated, the type of brake system and blocks used, the length of time since the car was last treated and the oiling and greasing requirements of the equipment, particularly of the motor bogie. In the days before the provision of the blow-out shop, smouldering and spontaneous combustion fires occurred under cars quite often, particularly under the body headstocks because of the accumulation of dirt and grease.

The new self-contained Trimming Shop was arranged with separate incoming and outgoing platforms and the working area located between the two. There was a storage area with special bins, each one capable of holding a complete car

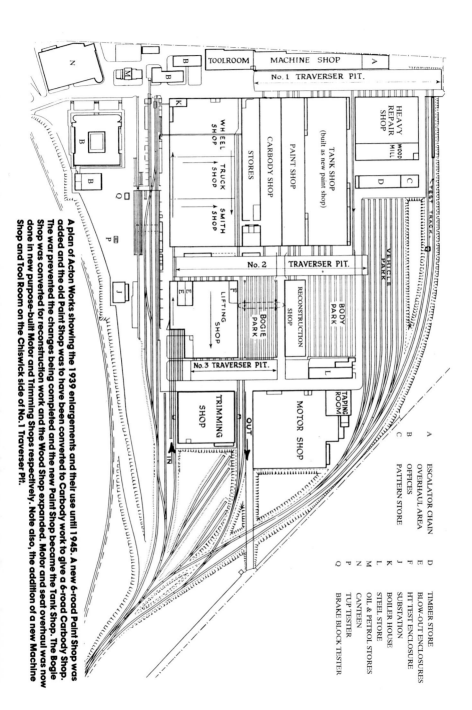

A plan of Acton Works showing the 1939 enlargements and their use until 1945. A new 6-road Paint Shop was added and the old Paint Shop was to have been converted to Carbody work to give a 6-road Carbody Shop. The war prevented the changes being completed and the new Paint Shop became the Tank Shop. The Bogie Shop was converted for reconstruction work and the Wood Shop expanded. Motor and seat overhaul was now done in new purpose-built Motor and Trimming Shops respectively. Note also, the addition of a new Machine Shop and Tool Room on the Chiswick side of No. 1 Traverser Pit.

A   ESCALATOR CHAIN
B   OVERHAUL AREA
C   OFFICES
    PATTERN STORE

D   TIMBER STORE
E   BLOW-OUT ENCLOSURES
F   HT TEST ENCLOSURE
J   SUBSTATION
K   BOILER HOUSE
L   STEEL STORE
M   OIL & PETROL STORES
N   CANTEEN
P   TUP TESTER
Q   BRAKE BLOCK TESTER

set of seats. Overhead conveyors were provided to carry the individual seats around the shop and from the dismantling area through a seat cleaning machine to the storage area. Manhandling of seats was kept to a minimum by the provision of these conveyors. One was provided which circulated around the seat trimming areas where the skilled trimmers carried out their work.

The storage bins were stacked in two tiers and were handled by a special fork lift truck. The bins were provided with drop sides so that, when a car was placed on the outgoing road, the appropriate bin could be placed in a position where the seats could be wheeled into the car for refitting with the minimum of physical handling.

The hard wearing moquette specified for Underground cars did not usually require replacement in under less than fifteen years, so only a proportion of the cars received for overhaul required retrimming (replacement of seat covering moquette). The main function of the Trimming Shop was therefore the cleaning and repair of seating and then the storage of it until the overhauled cars were ready to receive it.

The fourth new shop was an extension of the main building of the Works. This was to become the new Paint Shop and had six tracks, capacity enough to deal with a fleet of up to 5,000 vehicles. Unlike the old Paint Shop, which had been equipped with continuously moving chains, the new shop was planned on the basis of only moving vehicles along the tracks at time intervals as required.

The provision of the new shop would have allowed the old Paint Shop to be modified to form an extension to the Carbody Shop but the second world war broke out before this could be done. Up to that time, progress on the expansion of the works had been good. The new Tool Room and Machine Shop were completed in 1938 and an extension to the Wood Shop was built. In 1939 most of the building work had been completed and the new Motor Shop and Taping Room were in operation.

The Wood Shop was given a three-road extension, increasing the number of tracks there from seven to ten. Behind the shop a test track was built along the boundary of the site all the way to the throat of the works fan at Acton Town station. This and the extension to the Wood Shop meant that the southern boundary of the works was extended 120 feet into the District Railway sports ground.

The outbreak of the war meant that the Works did not get all its extensions into railway overhaul production until some years later. The war saw the new Paint Shop in use as a workshop for the overhaul of Bren Gun carriers and Sherman tanks. It henceforth became known as the Tank Shop. The ordnance, engines and gearboxes on the vehicles were removed and sent elsewhere for attention but other parts were replaced as necessary and replacement ordnance and engines were returned for fitting at Acton. The Sherman tanks were moved to and from the Works on flat wagons hauled from West Kensington goods yard by LT steam engines. The Bren Gun carriers were sometimes delivered by road. They were allowed to use public roads because they were comparatively light vehicles not destructive of the road surfaces.

Upper Left **The seating repair facility at Acton was known as the Trimming Shop. A dedicated building for this work was opened in 1939. The seats can be seen on the conveyor which carried them round the shop to distribute the work.** 23795-1

Left **Part of the Trimming Shop was devoted to seat cleaning. Beating, scrubbing and drying were included in the cleaning process. Here, a mechanical scrubber is cleaning a seat.** U8163

Other war work was carried out in the Machine Shop. It involved the manufacture of parts for London Aircraft Productions. This was a consortium of organisations, including London Transport, which was engaged in the production of Wellington bombers. At the same time, the Motor Shop was engaged in the repair of electric motors from the Royal Navy.

Apart from these excursions into the war effort, Acton Works continued its main effort of keeping the Underground rolling stock operating satisfactorily and safely. There were, however, some relaxations of standards. For example, wheel tyres were allowed to wear down further than normal. Motor wheels on Standard Tube Stock were 36 inches in diameter when new and they were normally replaced when they had worn down to 32½ inches. They were now allowed to run down to 32 inches. This did cause some problems with cracked tyres during the cold winter of 1939-40 but, in general, provided some useful maintenance savings.

Two major work schemes involving the rolling stock were introduced as a result of the war. One was the provision of 'reading lights' inside the cars. They consisted of four or five very dim bulbs known as Osglim lamps. They were actually neon lamps, very similar to night lights used for children, and had been used for years as the guard's pilot lights on Standard Tube Stock to indicate that the doors were closed. A set of these lamps placed along the ceiling of each car and switched on when the train ran out into the open at night was to ensure that passengers could see enough to move about without distress. Although they were called reading lights, the light was so poor that this was virtually a euphemism. The normal lighting could not be used as a result of the need to maintain the blackout precautions against air raids.

The work of fitting the reading lights was done at depots but the battens and wiring loops were prepared on a production basis at Acton and were dispatched in sets, complete with switches, to the depots. The first train was fitted with reading lights at Golders Green in late 1939 and all trains had been equipped by the winter of 1940.

The second major scheme for the rolling stock in wartime was the provision of window netting. When the serious bombing of London started in the winter of 1940, it was considered that the risk of casualties from flying glass was greater than that from the actual bombs and a series of experiments started to try to find a splinter proof arrangement.

Many of the experiments to find the best arrangement were carried out at Acton and, when the right system was established, Acton provided the depots with the materials to do the job. A curtain netting material was found suitable for the purpose. It was made to adhere to the windows with a clear varnish. A diamond-shaped opening was cut in the centre of each piece of netting to allow some view of the outside world and the raw edges were covered with a putty-like substance.

Acton Works was considerably affected by the manpower shortage produced by the call-up to arms. The working week was increased to 56 hours in 5½ days and women began to replace men in both unskilled and semi-skilled work. The craft trade unions also agreed to some semi-skilled employees being promoted to skilled work even though they had not undergone the customary apprenticeship. This was to lead to much trouble in the years after the war.

A rare photograph showing the interior of the Bogie Shop in use as a repair facility for Bren Gun Carriers. Note the large number of women employed because of the war.

Metropolitan electric locomotive No.3 at the head of a train of low loader wagons carrying Sherman Tanks. The train is about to leave Acton Works on 26th July 1944. The new Paint Shop, renamed the Tank Shop, was used for the overhaul of Sherman Tanks during the latter part of the second world war. U35851

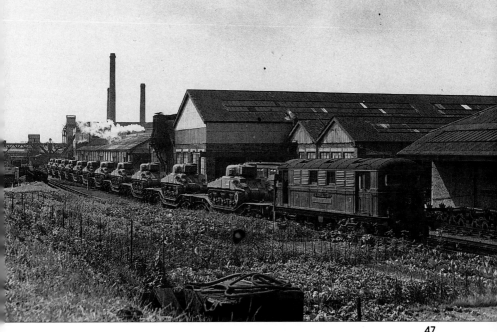

RECONSTRUCTION ACTIVITIES

In the years immediately following the electrification of the District and the opening of the tube lines in the early 1900s, the rolling stock was new and rebuilding or conversion of cars (reconstruction as it was to become known at Acton) was thus of a very spasmodic nature. The District was the first line to carry out reconstruction in a big way with the conversion of some trailers to control trailers in 1908 and with the removal of the luggage compartments from certain of its motor cars during the period up to 1914. Immediately after the first world war, the District had to carry out large scale reconstruction work on the bodies of its wooden trailer cars to keep them in a serviceable condition. Since Acton Works had not yet been built, all of these jobs were done at Ealing Common.

Very little of this sort of work was done on the tube lines until the programme for rebuilding the Piccadilly gate stock motor cars for air-door operation in the period 1920-24. However, the bulk of this job was contracted out to the Cammell Laird and Gloucester companies. Some twenty motor cars were converted for use with forty new trailers built in 1920 by Cammell Laird.

Even after the first part of the Acton Works complex was opened in 1922, reconstruction work continued to be done elsewhere. The conversion of eight Central London motor cars with more modern electrical equipment for use on the Ealing service (the so-called Yorke conversions) was done at Wood Lane and the conversion of the whole Central London stock to air-doors was done, as already mentioned, at the UCC works at Feltham.

With the 1928 expansion of Acton Works, two roads in the Lifting Shop were allocated to what was then described as general repairs. This was not really reconstruction work, being mainly concerned with mechanical and electrical modifications. Body reconstruction was done in the new Wood Shop. Within a year of its opening in 1931, the Bogie Shop was also being used for reconstruction work instead of bogie storage. Overhauled bogies were now stored in the open and motor trucks, which had their traction motors refitted during the overhaul process, were provided with tarpaulin covers for protection. When the programme for the fitting of electro-pneumatic brakes to the tube cars began in 1932, there was not enough room in the Wood and Lifting Shops for all the cars undergoing modifications so a standing area for six cars was provided to accommodate this work in the Bogie Shop, together with bench space for the associated off-car work.

In order to get the correct bogies from the outside storage area (henceforth known as the Bogie Park), a Goliath type crane was installed over the eight tracks of the park. It could lift a bogie out of a line of them stored on any of the tracks. It enabled a satisfactory supply to be maintained to the Lifting Shop. Until this crane was made available, a considerable amount of shunting of bogies, using the traversers, was necessary. This was not only time consuming but required extra space in the Bogie Park.

Opposite **A double-ended shunting locomotive built at Acton from the driving ends of two Hampstead Line gate stock motor cars in 1930. It was numbered L10 and had a special coupler and centre buffer which could be raised or lowered as necessary to fit surface or tube stock.** U8167

The bogie park at Acton in the early 1950s showing cars of O, P and 1938 Tube Stocks stored at the rear. A Goliath crane was installed to allow rapid access to bogies stored here. LT37

A unique job carried out in this Reconstruction Shop, following its conversion from the Bogie Shop, was the conversion of six Metropolitan Railway saloon stock cars for the experimental Metadyne train. Following some trials on a 2-car District train, the conversion work was begun in September 1934 and continued into the summer of 1935. Two spaces were allocated in the shop for almost a year while the cars were worked on. The train paved the way for the large order of Metadyne equipped O and P Stock trains ordered for the District and Metropolitan Lines.

Another job undertaken in the Reconstruction Shop was the rebuilding of old Central London motor cars into sleet locomotives. The bulk of the work was carried out during the first two years of the second world war between 1939 and 1940. The job was done by cutting two cars in half and placing the leading sections back to back and inserting a centre piece to form one double-ended locomotive.

It was intended that 20 such locomotives should be obtained in this way but, in the end, only 18 were made. An experimental, diesel-electric locomotive was also built by the same method. This system of reconstruction had first been tried in 1930 on two Hampstead gate stock motor cars which were rebuilt at Acton into a shunting locomotive (L10) for the Works.

Another reconstruction job completed during the war was the conversion of a number of old Metropolitan saloon cars. They were converted into dormitory and canteen cars for use by the 'Bevan Boys', conscripts who had opted for work in

A number of Underground cars were damaged during the second world war. The former Bogie Shop is here being used in April 1941 for reconstruction work of various types including the repair of a damaged P Stock motor car. On the left can be seen the end of the ill-fated diesel-electric locomotive DEL120 which was built at Acton in 1941. U32819

the mines in preference to going into the army. Later in the war Acton also did some special modifications on road breakdown vehicles for the US Army Transportation Corps in preparation for the invasion of Europe. Most of the latter work was done in the Wood Shop.

As a result of the war, work on the 1935-40 New Works Programme had ceased completely by early in 1941, although it had already been run down to a certain extent over the previous 12 months. At the end of the war in 1945, some of this work was restarted. The extensions to the Central Line were given priority. The Standard Tube Stock for the extensions had been displaced from the Northern Line by the delivery of the 1938 Tube Stock and had been stored in the partly completed depots at Ruislip and Hainault.

Initially, as many as possible of the stored cars had been kept under cover but the depot buildings were soon requisitioned for war work at both places. Ruislip was used for the assembly of Oerlikon anti-aircraft guns and Hainault, following the entry of the United States into the war, for the assembly of railway wagons for the US Corps of Transportation. The wagons were to be transferred to Europe after the invasion so that traffic could be restored on continental railways as soon as possible. As a result of the requisitioning of the depot sheds, the stored Underground cars were moved out into the open. Cars intended for the Central Line were also stored at Morden, Edgware, Golders Green and Neasden.

By the end of the war, with much of Acton having been involved in non-railway work, there was a need for a reorganisation to restore normal production and to make provision for the overhaul of the stored Central Line cars. Some of the cars had been stored in the open for up to seven years. Not only were many cars suffering from air raid damage but many had been wilfully vandalised. They were also suffering from the ravages of weather and neglect. Their preparation for service was to involve a large reconstruction programme.

The vacation of the 'Tank' Shop in 1945 allowed the area to be prepared for rolling stock work and, in April 1946, work started on the rehabilitation of the Central Line Standard Stock.

The cars were constructed mainly of steel and there had been considerable penetration of water during their time in storage. Rust was a big problem and much effort was expended in renewing floor plates and door tracks. Rubber in its various forms: door edges, brake hosepipes and even rubber covered cables had seriously deteriorated and had to be replaced. Traction motors, compressors and other electrical items had to have a complete overhaul. Extra staff had to be recruited to enable the work to be done in time for the opening of the extensions. Cars were dealt with at the rate of about five per week and, by the end of 1947, of the total of 340 cars to be done, 300 were completed. This work was done in parallel with normal overhaul work which, at the time, was running at just over 20 cars per week.

The 1938-built Paint Shop in use as the Reconstruction Shop in 1946. The majority of the cars are Standard Tube cars taken out of wartime storage for rehabilitation. They were to be used on the new eastern and western extensions of the Central Line. U38570

Work on the bodies of the Central Line cars was undertaken mainly in the new Reconstruction Shop, as the 'Tank' Shop had become. The area was organised to give six standing spaces on the 400ft length of each of the three roads in the shop. Two of the tracks were confined to reconstruction work while the third became the 'finishing road'. All cars, including those on normal overhaul, passed along this road after painting to allow items of equipment, which might be damaged if fitted before repainting, to be re-installed. It also allowed extra time for the finishing varnish to harden and avoided delays in the Lifting Shop.

As soon as the first two Central Line trains were finished, they were put into service to confirm, as soon as possible, that the level of work undertaken was sufficient to meet requirements. Inevitably, there had been a conflict between how much to spend to make the trains perfect to ensure reliability and how much to save by re-using existing equipment and materials. In the event, the cost of the rehabilitation work was not far short of the cost of buying completely new cars but it is very doubtful that sufficient new stock could have been obtained in time for the completion of the work on the extensions. A further two years would have been necessary and this would have delayed the opening of the extensions by an unacceptable amount.

An interesting problem arose with the coupling and drawgear of the Standard Stock on the Central Line. When constructed, the line had been built on what was called the saw tooth arrangement. The stations were built at the top of humps with 1 in 30 inclines down and 1 in 60 inclines up to help acceleration out of the platform and retardation into the platform. It gave a natural power saving arrangement.

It was found that the transition from one incline to another was too sharp and that the Standard Stock couplers were being subjected to severe cyclical bending. This resulted in a spate of fractured drawbars. This was a serious failure because it caused the train to part into two sections — a 'breakaway'. The problem had not occurred on the old Central London cars because they had link and pin couplers.

It was decided to replace the drawbars on some 400 Standard Stock cars with improved material. This required each one to be removed and sent to Acton for the shank to be replaced. A special working area had to be set up to deal with them during the programme, which lasted six months.

Rehabilitation of the Central Line stock achieved the objectives of the time in getting it ready for the extended services but the renovated cars were never as reliable as expected and they caused considerable increases in the general costs of maintenance and stretched the resources of Acton Works over the years. They were withdrawn in 1960-3, being replaced by the 1959/62 Tube Stock.

Following the completion of the Central Line rehabilitation work, reconstruction work was moved to the old Carbody Shop and car body overhaul was henceforth done in the former Reconstruction Shop. The next job undertaken in the new Reconstruction Shop was the consolidation of the 1938 Tube Stock fleet. It had been decided to rebuild three trains of the streamlined 1935 Tube Stock cars so that they could become part of the 1938 Stock fleet. It was also planned to incorporate some stored cars of 1938 Stock and a batch of new cars, known as 1949 Tube Stock, into the 1938 Stock fleet so as to form 183 x 7 car trains. A considerable amount of work was involved because many cars were non-standard. Some had been intended for use in 9-car trains. In addition, a new type of car, known as an Uncoupling Non-Driving Motor car (UNDM), a motor car without a full driving position, was introduced. Some 22 of these cars were converted at Acton from vehicles which had been in the 9-car trains.

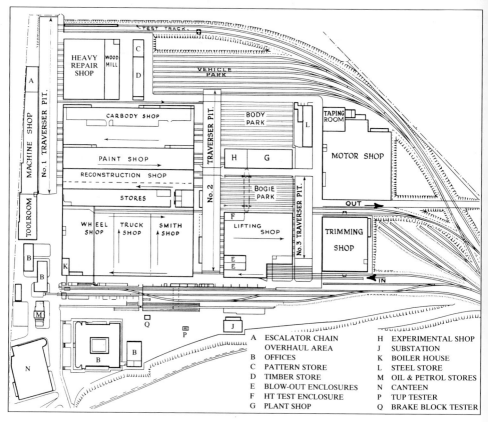

A plan of Acton Works in its heyday, showing the reorganised layout of 1946. The Carbody Shop has become the Reconstruction Shop whilst the Tank Shop has become the Carbody Shop. The former Bogie Shop has lost the reconstruction work and is now used for experimental work and plant. The works remained substantially as shown here until the rebuilding of 1986-8 although the Reconstruction Shop became an additional Carbody Shop when the amount of reconstruction work reduced.

In 1950, with work on the 1935 Tube Stock rebuilding completed, a new programme of rehabilitation was started on the F Stock. This consisted of 99 cars, built in 1920 for the District, which were to be transferred to the Metropolitan Line for working the Uxbridge service. Before transfer, they were to pass through the Reconstruction Shop. The work included almost a complete rewire. Both power and control cables were involved. Many were the originals, which had insulation which deteriorated with age. The first reconstructed train went into service on 27th February 1951 and the stock lasted on the Metropolitan line until 1963.

Reconstruction work continued right to the end of Acton as the main car overhaul works. The preparation of tube cars of 1960 Stock for the first full-scale trials of Automatic Train Operation was done at Acton and the Standard Tube Stock cars intended for the Isle of Wight were given a special overhaul there after their withdrawal from service in London. More recently, during the mid-1980s, the conversion of the 1973 Tube Stock and the A Stock for one-man-operation was also undertaken at Acton.

1938 Tube, Standard Tube and District Q27 (formerly K) stocks in the Carbody Shop in 1949. This area had been the Reconstruction Shop for the rehabilitation of the Central Line Standard Stock but was converted for normal overhaul production in 1948. HD780-2

Rehabilitation of the F Stock was undertaken at Acton Works during 1951-53. Cars of this stock can be seen here in the Reconstruction Shop (the former Carbody Shop) in September 1952. One of the jobs done during this work was the replacement of the old type wooden door for a new cast aluminium type. Following their rehabilitation, the F Stock cars were transferred from the District to the Metropolitan. U53769

The Carbody Shop in the 1930s showing the mechanical bench area with a District Line F Stock car on the assembly road behind. The mechanical benches overhauled brake valves, door engines and similar items. Note the raised coat rack hoisted into the roof. U4880

TECHNOLOGICAL CHANGES

When Acton Works first opened in 1922, the advances made in machine tools and the handling of heavy steel during the first world war were already available, as well as the progressive methods of manufacture developed in the United States, first for armaments and then for motor cars. However, there was still a need for craftsmen in workshops, especially at Acton.

One of the most important trades in a railway overhaul works at this time was the blacksmith. Many of the wearing parts of the rolling stock were made of wrought iron and steel and forging of the replacement parts was a large scale activity requiring a number of skilled men. Welding was in its infancy but riveting, both hot and cold, was required, especially in truck frame repairs. By 1922, many trucks were being made of plate and angles riveted together in place of the earlier designs using forgings and castings bolted together.

The need for a large blacksmiths shop continued until new designs of rolling stock eliminated the single brake cylinder requiring rigging between the cylinder mounted on the underframe and the brake blocks on the trucks. This change took place with the introduction of the 1938 Tube Stock, where each brake block had its own brake cylinder, virtually eliminating rigging.

Another common trade in the railway industry at the time was that of bodymaker. Car bodies on the District and Metropolitan were originally made of wood and, even with the steel bodies used on the tube lines, a considerable amount of finishing consisted of wood panels and mouldings. During the 1960s, this sort of material was replaced by plastics, not even requiring painting.

Both skilled and semi-skilled fitters were employed for mechanical work. Much of the general assembly work did not require much attention to close fits and limits and could be done by semi-skilled men. This factor caused railway fitters to be given a soubriquet of either 'hammer and chisel fitters' or 'half-inch fitters'.

Some skilled men were required for work such as that to do with brake valves. Even in 1922, Westinghouse brake valves of various types were robust in construction but delicate in operation and required skilled maintenance. In addition, skilled turners were needed to operate the high quality machine tools used to provide replacement parts and they were backed up by equally skilled tool fitters providing the gauges for checking the various details. The need for their employment grew rather than diminished as the equipment carried on the rolling stock increased, as brake equipment got more complicated and as air operated doors were introduced.

In the early days of electric traction, even electrical fitters were not required to be particularly skilled since much of their work was more mechanical than electrical. They were required to deal with repairs to the mechanically operated contactors and circuit breakers but their electrical knowledge was confined to an understanding of how they worked and their basic function in an electrical circuit. Some electrical assembly and checking work of a more repetitive nature was entrusted to semi-skilled staff.

The GE69 traction motor most common on the Underground at the time of the opening of the Works was one of the earliest geared designs in use and was

Brake cylinder parts being overhauled at the assembly end of the car body roads of the original workshops. Behind the work area, a B Stock trailer car with 1st and 3rd class accommodation is ready to move out to No. 1 traverser for moving to the assembly area where it will be reunited with its bogies. Note the collars and ties worn by a majority of the shop floor staff. U1656

unreliable compared with later designs. The average failure rate was about 50% per annum and armatures required rewinding approximately every three years. A central repair shop was originally established at Golders Green Depot and remained there until 1924, when the staff and facilities were transferred to Acton Works. Rewinding was done in the motor area of the main building until the 1938 reorganisation when it was transferred to the new Motor Shop.

The demand for skilled armature winders was very high from the beginning and, although the reliability of motors improved with the introduction of more modern designs of motors with interpoles, the number of motors per train increased and armature winders continued to be in demand. On the Piccadilly Line, for example, the number of motors on a train was four until 1932, when it was increased to six. With the introduction of the 1938 Tube Stock on the Northern Line the number of motors increased to ten per train. In addition, more rotating machinery was introduced with the appearance of motor generators for auxiliary circuits and, in 1936, the Metadyne machine for the O and P Stocks. Nowadays, the reliability of traction motors has improved to such an extent that very few armatures ever require rewinding during a service life of over 35 years.

One of the most significant technological changes which took place on Underground rolling stock was the introduction of ball and roller bearings in place of white metal bearings on axles, traction motors and other rotating parts. This innovation not only affected the amount of work required by Acton personnel but also increased the reliability of the rolling stock in service.

Roller bearing axleboxes were first tried by the Metropolitan Railway on a group of compartment stock motor coaches (T Stock) in 1930 and, in 1934, a batch of ten Piccadilly Line motor cars was delivered with them. The pairs of wheels used in these trials were always special and could only be dealt with for tyre turning on a specially adapted wheel lathe. In 1936, however, a roller bearing with a pull-off axlebox was developed in collaboration with the firms of Hoffman and SKF so that the roller bearing fitted wheelsets could be dealt with for wheel turning and other requirements exactly as a plain bearing axle. All rolling stock built subsequently for Underground service had roller bearing axleboxes.

In spite of the introduction of ball and roller bearings, the plain white metal bearing lasted for many more years on the Underground until the withdrawal of the last of the District Line Q Stock in 1971. The axle bearing transferred the weight of the car body and bogie to the top of the axle. It was essential to maintain proper lubrication of the surfaces of the bearing and the axle as the wheelset turned or else the bearing would quickly overheat and cause what was known as a 'hot box'. To provide the lubrication, an oil-soaked wool 'dolly' was packed into the box (the axlebox) surrounding the axle and bearing. It was fed, by capillary action, from oil in a reservoir at the base of the axlebox. Repacking axleboxes was a laborious and unpleasant maintenance task. The axleboxes required regular checking to ensure that there was enough oil, that the wool was properly packed and that the bearing was not worn. Renewal of worn white metal bearings was a continuous headache for the organisation.

White metal was also used originally for the traction motor bearings. A programme of replacement of armature bearings was carried out on the more modern motors during the early 1930s when a special boring machine was used at Acton to modify the end housings to take ball and roller bearings. Motor suspension bearings on axles could not be modified so roller bearing systems did not appear on motor axles until the introduction of new stock in 1936. Before this, Acton had to produce over 2000 remetalled motor suspension bearings a week, including ones for depots and for overhauled cars passing through the Works.

A District Line L Stock trailer being lifted from its bogies circa 1933. This car has both first and third class accommodation and it has hand-worked doors. Although all the tube lines had air doors by this time, the District and Metropolitan still had hand operated doors. Many cars were converted at Acton but hand doors were not completely eliminated until the late-1950s. U14170

The elimination of white metal motor suspension bearings came with the introduction of the 1935 experimental Tube Stock and the O Stock. A roller suspension sleeve, to which the motor was bolted, was designed to fit around the axle. It changed the lubricating methods from frequent oiling to longer term grease application and it permitted the bearing to run with very long periods between removal from the axle.

Further progress in eliminating maintenance problems was made in the 1950s with improvements in truck design. The ironmongery on trucks was simplified by the introduction of rubber in shear for springing. Rubber springing was first tried experimentally on the District Line in the early 1950s and was then applied to the three trains of the 1956 Tube Stock. Subsequently, it was applied to all new rolling stock on the Underground. The combination of this, with the introduction of welding, simplified steel construction and aluminium castings into truck design considerably reduced the maintenance requirements.

The process of eliminating as many moving parts as possible was continued to include smaller items of equipment as well as the larger ones. An example of this trend was door interlocks. From the introduction of air operated doors in

The first unpainted aluminium cars entered service on the District Line in 1952. One of the earliest of these, an R49 car No. 22680, can be seen here on the second traverser installed in the No.2 pit in the mid-1950s. The introduction of unpainted car bodies was to be the beginning of the end for Acton Works 1667/2

the 1920s until the 1950s, the closed door was proved by an electrical contact, activated by a pin, on the door engine arm on the earliest equipment or on the door itself on the later equipment. The contacts were mechanical and not only had to be accurately set to ensure that no more than a half-inch opening was possible but had also to be regularly cleaned.

The introduction of encapsulated mercury interlocks to perform the proving function eliminated at one stroke both a labour intensive maintenance job and the setting of a fixed replacement period for the equipment.

In the same way, the introduction of magnetic amplifiers for the regulation of motor generator voltage has eliminated the moving carbon systems which were used to perform this function. The moving carbon regulators required regular and accurate resetting and the carbons also needed replacing at set intervals.

In 1952 the Underground introduced their first unpainted aluminium cars, of R Stock, into service on the District. By the end of the decade, all new tube and surface stock cars had unpainted aluminium exteriors. This sounded the death knell of the Paint Shop at Acton Works and made it possible to consider extending the overhaul cycle again. On this, more later.

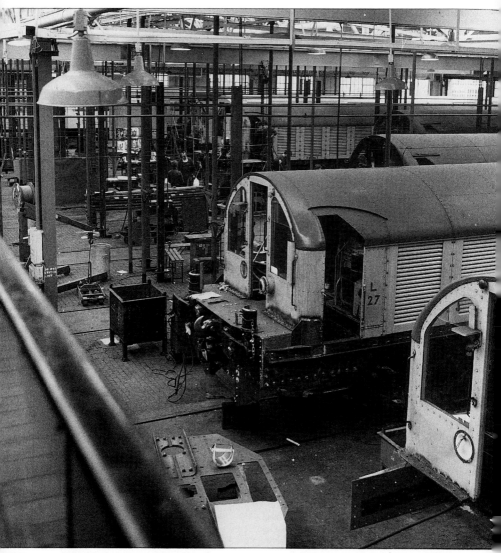

The interior of the Wood Shop as seen in the early 1980s showing battery locomotives undergoing collision repairs. The Wood Shop was used for this type of work throughout the life of Acton.
23795-13

ACTON WORKS AT ITS OPTIMUM

Although it was the intention that Acton Works should return to normality at the end of the second world war in 1945, it was some time before this was fully achieved. As we have seen, the first major change was the conversion of the Tank Shop into a new Reconstruction Shop. At the same time, the old Reconstruction Shop, the former Bogie Shop, became the Plant Shop and the Experimental Shop.

The maintenance of the plant used in the Works and at depots had been scattered throughout the Works, mostly in odd corners of the main building. It was now brought together in one building. There was quite a large amount of elderly equipment still in use and a centralised facility had become important in keeping it operational.

One of the jobs carried out by the plant section was the conversion of the alternating current supply to the Works from 33⅓Hz to 50Hz. It was decided to do this as part of the programme to modernise the Lots Road Power Station, from which the power supply for the Works had been taken since its opening in 1922. At that time, 33⅓Hz was considered to be kinder to the rotary converters in the traction sub-stations needed to provide 630 volts DC for the train supply and had therefore been adopted as standard. By 1962, the introduction of mercury arc rectifiers to provide traction current enabled the more efficient 50Hz industrial frequency to be used on LT. The frequency change rendered most of the AC motors fitted to the works machinery obsolete and they had to be renewed. The opportunity was also taken to convert some DC driven equipment to standard frequency AC drives.

The Wood Shop was extended under the 1935-40 New Works Programme. It was originally located on the south side of the main Works building and with its eastern wall set back about 80 feet from the boundary line of the main building. It was extended eastwards to the boundary line to allow two cars on each existing road instead of one, and southwards to allow an increase in the number of roads from seven to ten. The space available for cars undergoing extensive body conversions or heavy repairs was increased from seven vehicles to seventeen.

At the western, or Ealing, end of the shop was the Wood Mill. This was a production shop where all wooden parts were made including shoebeams, floor lagging, mouldings and doors. Car doors originally had wooden frames and panels, but after 1912 most stocks had steel panels on wood frames. In the 1920s the first aluminium doors appeared. On more modern stocks, much of the wooden framing and panelling was replaced by plastics and, nowadays, these are being replaced by aluminium to meet more stringent fire safety regulations.

Shoebeams were originally made of oak or teak but later were of laminated timber to a specially rigorous LT specification. The laminated blocks were shaped and machined by the Wood Shop into beams to fit the various types of stock. The overhaul of shoebeams was carried out in a special area of the Lifting Shop after their removal from incoming cars. They were stored there until they rejoined the cars after overhaul. Only replacement beams were provided from the Wood Mill.

The Acton Works complex from the air in 1952 looking east towards Chiswick Works, which can just be seen in the distance. The District and Piccadilly Lines are to the left and on the extreme left is the single line branch to South Acton. Aerofilms A44728/52

Until the early 1960s escalator steps were all fitted with renewable wooden cleats. The Wood Mill supplied new cleats, which were made of maple or purple heart timber specially treated with fire proofing. Special equipment was developed for taking out screws with badly worn heads and for rapid reassembly.

The Wood Shop had always been concerned with heavy body repairs which could not be undertaken within the normal overhaul cycle time. Much of its work was concerned with collision damage repairs, although its first major job was the 1920s refurbishment of wooden District stock. Many of the trailer cars suffered from sagging centres and dropped ends, largely due to their poor construction. They were built with wooden frames, badly fitted when built, and some sagged by as much as three inches from true. The motor cars had steel underframes so that they had the strength to carry the underfloor electrical equipment and they did not suffer from such serious troubles. From late in 1928 until early in 1930, over 80 wooden trailer cars had their frames packed up and were fitted with a continuous length of angled steel on the underside of the main timber solebars. Many of these cars lasted until the arrival of the Q Stock in 1938-40.

The Wood Shop continued to carry out heavy repairs even though later cars were made of steel. After the second world war and the subsequent alterations to the Works, the Wood Shop became officially known as the Heavy Repair Shop, although the old name continued in use amongst the staff for a number of years afterwards.

Throughout its life, the Wood Shop had to deal with dropped ends. Many minor collisions, and what were called 'rough shunts', caused damage to the driving ends of cars. The Standard Stock, with their joggled solebars over the motor bogies, were particularly susceptible to having dropped ends, as were the battery locomotives with their high frames and low cab floors. Over the years, many of the battery locomotives had to have prolonged treatment for dropped ends.

The long narrow Machine Shop and Tool Room building flanking the Acton to Kew Bridge railway line saw little major change after the war. At the far end of the shop, however, an area previously used for servicing soda-acid fire extinguishers (superseded by the water CO_2 type, which were serviced by their manufacturers) was progressively developed for renewal of escalator drive chain.

The Machine Shop had long had a commitment to build replacement 18inch chain units for the older 'L' type escalators but, by the early 1950s, the chains of the heavy duty 'M' series machines installed in the 1930s were wearing out and a major renewal programme was required. A design study showed that it would be practicable to rebore the existing link plates to suit new bushes, pins and rollers manufactured to revised dimensions. The chain was therefore removed from escalators in 8ft lengths. After reconditioning, the chain was returned to site in galvanised steel containers specially made for the task. The exact length of every eight foot piece of chain was accurately registered because each escalator had two chains and it was important that there should be no creep along the length of one side compared to the other. Later, a modified 'L' type chain was produced in 6ft lengths.

Dedicated cleaning plant, presses, conveyors and other devices were laid out in the escalator chain area and it became a very efficient facility. In parallel with this development, the rest of the Machine Shop saw an increase of precision work demanding special tooling and inspection to produce pins and bushes for all kinds of repairs. At this time the first multi-spindle automatic lathe was installed to be followed by another and larger machine. In later years, as the older types of rolling stock were phased out, the demand for pins and bushes fell dramatically because the new cars had neither brake rigging nor steel suspension systems. Modern cars had brake cylinders for every block and bogies had rubber suspension.

In order to ensure a continual supply of trained craftsmen, especially mechanical fitters, electrical fitters and bodymakers, the training of apprentices had been established in Underground workshops from the earliest years. At Acton, a specially built apprentice training centre was opened on 7th August 1958 by the then Chairman of London Transport, Sir John Elliot.

The centre comprised a new single storey building divided into a workshop area, a lecture room and self-contained amenities. The centre was established to provide apprentice training for the whole of the Chief Mechanical Engineer's Department which, at that time, encompassed Acton Works, the rolling stock depots and the lifts and escalators department. Craft apprentices had always been encouraged in the department and W.A. Agnew, the first Chief Mechanical Engineer, provided a trophy — the Agnew Trophy — which was awarded annually to the best apprentice.

The success of this centre led to the provision of a larger facility to train apprentices for all the engineering departments. This was constructed on spare ground adjacent to Acton Town station and was opened in 1972.

With the transfer of the apprentice training to the new school, the original building was modified to become the Electronics Repair Shop. Such a dedicated facility became essential after the introduction of Automatic Train Operation on the Victoria Line in 1968 and even more so later with the use of train equipment panels and other electronic devices used on the 1973 Tube Stock and subsequent types.

The interior of the staff canteen in 1924. A glance at the menus hanging on the wall shows that they, like the building, changed little during the life of the works, although the building was extended during the 1939 expansion. U1648

SOCIAL CHANGES

A railway operates 24 hours a day, seven days a week, and it is necessary to provide staff, even after traffic hours, in order to achieve this. For rolling stock, it was always necessary to provide some staff for maintenance work around the clock. In general, this staff was needed to carry out cleaning and examination work while stock was stabled at night and to provide some attendance for train preparation work or call outs during early mornings and late evenings. The remaining work was carried out during normal hours in the depot workshops.

A division developed between the staff employed on shift duties and those employed in the workshops during normal daytime hours. The shift staff, called conciliation staff after the way in which their pay and conditions of service were agreed, were largely responsible for cleaning and ensuring that trains were fit for service before handing them over to operating staff. The line of promotion was from cleaner to car examiner. The examiner did just that; he examined the condition of the train and changed brake blocks, adjusted brake rigging, drained reservoirs (of water collected as a result of condensation), changed defective light bulbs, tested the safety devices (deadman and tripcock) and reported any defects which required 'shops attention' as it was called.

The shop staff, so called because they worked in the workshop, worked under engineering factory conditions. There were three basic levels — skilled, semi-skilled and unskilled or labourers. The skilled staff were mostly craftsmen who had served an apprenticeship under the nationally agreed system of training. The semi-skilled were employed as assistants or 'mates' for the skilled fitters as well as for carrying out the more routine and less complicated work. Each skilled trade had its own union which represented the interests of its own particular craft. A degree of rivalry existed between many of the unions and it was a long time before a joint approach was used when dealing with management. Even today, this rivalry, although much reduced, still exists in some trades.

Sometimes, this rivalry was taken to seemingly ridiculous limits. On the District Line, the hand operated doors of the early stocks were naturally maintained by bodymakers. With the advent of the more complicated, air-operated door systems introduced on the tube lines in the 1920s, mechanical fitters were employed to maintain the doors. When air doors were introduced to the District in 1938, mechanical fitters were given these doors too. The bodymakers, fearful of losing the work, protested. In a 'judgement of Solomon' decision, it was agreed that top hung doors, as used on the surface lines, would be maintained by bodymakers while doors relying on bottom tracks and only guided at the top, as used on the tube lines, would be maintained by mechanical fitters. When the R Stock arrived during the early 1950s, some cars had top-hung doors while the more modern ones had bottom-guided doors. The same rule was applied and it thus became necessary to employ two different trades to carry out the door maintenance on the same train.

The essential difference between the shop staff and the conciliation staff was that the shop staff were employed expressly for their specialist skills which were applicable in other industries apart from the railways, while the conciliation staff examiners had to be specially trained in the operation of the rolling stock. Their main task was to ensure that a complete train was ready for service. They were not craftsmen in the engineering sense of the word. However, they were required to do initial fault finding, insulation testing and tracing of circuit faults being common examples.

The two staffs were kept apart and, in an effort to ensure responsibility for safety, there was a rigid demarcation between their responsibilities at most depots. Some depots carried this to extreme levels while others, usually the smaller ones, had a high degree of co-operation which benefited both sides and helped to provide a better service.

All the repairs to equipment and changing of parts or machines was done by the shop staff. Each depot was provided with a limited range of machine tools to enable small jobs to be carried out when required to keep the stock running. Larger items, such as wheels, motors and compressors, were sent to Acton. The shop staff also carried out minor modifications to cars, usually when they were in the shop for another reason.

Acton Works was really a factory carrying out production work. The work was planned, long term and not connected with the day to day provision of the train service. For this reason, the work was carried out there during conventional factory hours. Like the depot shop staff, the Acton staff were employed for their skills in engineering work. Most of the traditional skills were used. Electrical, mechanical, bodymaking, trimming, carpentry, blacksmiths, toolmaking, turning, pipefitting and painting trades were all represented at Acton.

For almost 25 years following the establishment of Acton Works, the hours of work and general conditions of the shop staff were governed by the Industrial Court Award No.728 of 8th July 1922. At this time, the basic weekly rate of pay for a craftsman was 50 shillings (£2.50) while that of a labourer was 33 shillings (£1.65). Between these two grades there were numerous semi-skilled duties which merited a few pence differential in hourly rate to reward the extra knowledge or skill required and to encourage staff to try for promotion into these grades.

The majority of semi-skilled staff were generally recruited at unskilled level and subsequently promoted into semi-skilled positions as required. This was done by seniority, provided the candidate had the necessary experience. There was a tendency for lines of demarcation to arise in the semi-skilled grades in a similar way to those which existed in the skilled grades and lines of promotion developed along these lines. Staff tended to stay in these lines, since changing from one to another would result in a loss of seniority. However, staying in a particular line gave the men an assurance that, with experience, they could advance and it provided the management with a pool of suitably experienced staff with little need to provide expensive training. In fact, the training for semi-skilled staff mainly consisted of 'sitting with Buggins' and watching him do it until the foreman was satisfied that the operative could be left on his own.

At the top, a semi-skilled man could command a basic rate of 49 shillings (£2.45) per week, just below that of a craftsman. Of course, there were only a very limited number of staff to whom this rate was paid. One such grade was that of pipefitter, who learned his trade by example and practice. Similar rates were paid to top machinists controlling complicated machine tools.

For the ten years following the opening of Acton Works, there was very little inflation and the rates of pay set by the '728' award increased only gradually. However, in September 1932, following the impact of the great depression, all wages and salaries were subject to a 2½% cut, providing that the earnings of an adult member of staff did not fall below £2.50 per week or £130 per year. A further 2½% was deducted from those with a salary exceeding £750 per annum. At that time, this applied to only a few of the most senior staff at Acton.

Over the years, the differentials between the grades were gradually whittled away because wage increases had been mainly flat cash additions. By 1942, the rate for a craftsman had risen to £5 per week, double the level of the '728' award, while that for a labourer had risen from £1.65 to £4, considerably more than double. This had been the result of a deliberate policy throughout the industry of raising the rates for the lower paid. The effect of this was to reduce the differentials between the grades and to reduce the incentive for promotion into the semi-skilled grades. A powerful management tool to promote works loyalty was lost and subsequent years saw a worsening drift of good labour away from the Works to the newer factories and businesses setting up along the Great West Road and around Heathrow Airport.

The '728' award included a provision for holidays with pay (paid holidays being uncommon in industry at the time). After 12 months' service, an employee got two days' holiday which increased by one day per year of service until a total of five days had accrued. This did not include Christmas Day and Bank Holidays, which were days without work and without pay. The holiday was taken by the whole Works, which was shut down for a week, usually near the August Bank Holiday. The leave entitlement was increased to two weeks during the second world war and, subsequently, Bank Holidays were paid.

For virtually twenty years, the standard working week at Acton was 47 hours spread over 5½ days. The day began at 07.30 and ended at 17.00 with a one hour break for lunch (unpaid). Saturday finished at 12.00 midday. Occasionally it was necessary for a few staff to work at night to maintain plant or services. All hours worked between 18.00 and 06.00 were paid at a rate of time plus one sixth.

During the war, it became necessary to introduce a 56 hour week. This was established as three hours compulsory overtime for three evenings per week on top of the standard 47 hour week. At the end of hostilities, the hours were restored to the normal 47 per week and there was a considerable fall in the wages received by the staff. There was much agitation for some form of compensation. Eventually this was conceded, partly by improved basic rates, partly by an incentive bonus scheme and partly by a 'levelling up' agreement.

The 'levelling up' agreement of March 1947 arose because of the higher rates which existed for the road services staff employed on the bus side of the organisation at Chiswick and elsewhere.

It also served to eliminate some of the large number of differing basic rates then extant at Acton. In place of the variety which existed then, two levels of semi-skilled rates were introduced. They were known as semi-skilled 1 and semi-skilled 2 (SS1 and SS2 to everyone in the works). The rates per week were set at:

Craftsman	£6.125
SS1	£5.54
SS2	£5.35
Unskilled	£5.15

This arrangement proved unsatisfactory because a number of semi-skilled duties required considerable expertise and the staff concerned demanded additional rewards. To overcome the problem, a Semi-Skilled Staff Assessment Committee was established between the management and the Joint Committee of Unions. All work was assessed and given a grading number between one and ten. At the bottom was grade number one, the menial tasks of sweeping, fetching and carrying, while, at the top, was number ten, requiring the skill of a craftsman. It was agreed that work graded at nine or ten would be paid at the craftsman's rate while seven or eight would be paid at a rate above that of SS1. This new rate introduced a new grade of staff known as semi-skilled (starred), written as SS1*. The rate was £5.75. The new agreement came into force in May 1948.

In addition to the changes in staff grading, a bonus scheme was introduced in 1947. It was intended to give the staff something else to help a return to wartime earning levels and to provide a motive for improving production rates. The bonus calculation was, at first, solely based on the weekly throughput of cars in the various shops, points values being set in each shop for each type of car. The bonus was set at a general level of 13½% for a Works throughput of 23 cars per week.

It was agreed at the time of the introduction of this scheme that a more sophisticated scheme would be developed. Both the work on cars and on components would be broken down into basic operations and a working time set for each operation. On a shop by shop basis, this scheme took several years to develop and it was not until December 1950 that the first stage was introduced and 1955 before the Carbody Shop was included. Payments for 'idle time' or non-productive time which arose because of fluctuations in work levels were included in the scheme. Eventually, the system developed into a proper work study scheme. Depot shops staff and even conciliation staff were eventually included in the scheme.

There was not too much in the way of acrimony or industrial dispute during the setting up of these schemes although, from time to time, there was resistance to detailed stopwatch rating of work. It was always difficult to time precisely work of a maintenance nature and phrases such as 'averaging' or 'taking the rough with the smooth' became familiar terms during timing arguments. It must be said, however, that generous times were allowed for many of the tasks performed and, eventually, incentive bonus schemes became discredited.

There was also much pressure after the war from the trades unions to get the working week reduced. The first step in this direction took place on 21st May 1947 with the introduction of the 44-hour week and the elimination of Saturday mornings in the standard working week. The daily starting and finishing times had to be adjusted so that the lunch break was reduced to three-quarters of an hour, and Mondays finished at 17.15 instead of 17.00.

At the time, some disquiet was expressed about the availability of trains for the Monday morning service if no shops staff were available in the depots over the weekend. For a time, a Saturday morning roster of skilled staff was maintained at depots and the staff given time off during the week to compensate. It was subsequently found that this provision was not necessary and was discontinued.

The operation of the 44-hour week continued until 1961 when the working week was reduced to 42 hours. It was reduced again to 40 hours in February 1966. By this time each day finished at 16.15. Supervisors won a 38-hour week at this time, which caused administration problems for the management, since it was important that supervisors be on duty throughout the time that staff were working. The problem was resolved by granting an additional day of leave each month to supervisors.

Further reductions in the working week were granted in 1981 when it was reduced to 39 hours and in 1983 when it became 38 hours. By this time, Friday had become a working day without a lunch break and finished at 13.30.

During the period when the 'blue collar' working week was reduced from 47 to 38 hours, the 'white collar' workers already enjoyed a 38-hour week, a nine-to-five day with 3 hours on Saturday morning. Alternate Saturday mornings were worked from 1955 and they were later eliminated altogether. This eventually became a 35-hour week.

The trades unions played a big part in the social system at Acton Works. The National Union of Railwaymen (NUR) represented the grades of staff which worked on the railways, regardless of their skills, specialist training or knowledge. However, the craftsmen employed in the shops were usually represented by their own unions. At Acton, the Joint Trades Committee, set up in 1933 with the formation of the London Passenger Transport Board, was dominated by three unions. These were the Amalgamated Engineering Union (AEU), the Electrical Trades Union (ETU) and the National Union of Vehicle Builders (NUVB), to one of which most of the craftsmen in the Works belonged. There were some blacksmiths, wood machinists and sheet metal workers who belonged to their own unions but they would be represented by one of the 'big three' as necessary.

In spite of the fact that the skills represented by these unions were very important in the maintenance requirements of rolling stock, the total number of craftsmen employed in Acton Works was actually less than the total of the semi-skilled staff who were represented by the NUR. The Joint Trades Committee at Acton, which became known as the Allied Crafts Committee, formed a Joint Shops Committee with the NUR. The chairman of this committee was usually provided by the Allied Crafts while the secretary was provided by the NUR. They also combined with the NUR for negotiations with the senior management in what was called the Joint Committee of Unions.

The NUR, as the union of semi-skilled grades, was always looking for ways of getting the craftsman's rate of pay for the suitably skilled of their membership without the qualification of an apprenticeship. The introduction of electric welding as a required skill in the works was one way in which this was done. External recruitment was not possible in the London area so suitable staff were selected and trained. The skill achieved was subject to what was virtually a trade test and failure of the test resulted in removal from that sort of work. Tests were conducted annually by having established welders produce a test piece which was then subjected to tests at Chiswick Laboratory. These procedures were agreed with the NUR and promotion in this trade to craftsman's rate was achieved by some semi-skilled staff. The system worked very well and some of the welders employed at Acton and the depots were considered to be of a very high standard.

The NUR were not against the apprenticeship system for the training of skilled men but considered that loyalty, practice and experience should receive recognition through promotion. They insisted that seniority in the selection must be paramount provided that the candidate had the ability to perform the task. As the years went by and staff became harder to recruit and retain, it became obvious that the seniority rule predominated and that, in many cases, skills and ability tended to take a back seat.

The Electrical Trades Union (ETU) was both a craft and an industrial union to which anyone engaged in electrical work could belong. It had different grades of membership. It was possible for persons to be in the union who did not have the benefit of an apprenticeship to qualify to become an electrical fitter, as well as those who had been through the apprenticeship scheme.

There were also some craftsmen electrical fitters who were members of the NUR. They had qualified through the apprenticeship scheme run by the Underground. Since NUR members who had been recruited from the labouring

71

grades would have had the opportunity to become electrical fitters if they had been members of the ETU, they were given the same opportunity as the ETU members. They could, if suitably experienced, able and trained, become electrical craftsmen. The situation was recognised by both NUR and ETU and they came to an arrangement known as the 50/50 agreement whereby each electrical fitter vacancy was filled alternately by a member of each union. A panel of management and trade unions determined the qualification and suitability of each candidate.

The AEU craftsmen were not prepared to accept a corresponding arrangement for mechanical fitters with the NUR. This situation eventually led to the worst dispute ever to affect Acton Works. The problem arose from the difficulties created originally by the unusual circumstances of the second world war. The shortage of skilled staff caused by the war led to the Joint Trades Committee accepting a system whereby suitable semi-skilled staff performed a limited amount of the work previously done by craftsmen, especially in the area of mechanical fitting. The 'dilution agreement', as it was called, envisaged that, at the end of hostilities, the 'dilutees' would return to their semi-skilled duties. In the event, the difficulties of recruiting sufficient skilled staff, and the expansion of the Works, led to the 'dilutees' continuing to work as craftsmen and in no case was anyone forced to return to semi-skilled work. However, restrictions placed on their further promotion to leading fitter, chargehand or foreman, no matter how well qualified or experienced they had become, caused some resentment amongst the NUR members affected.

The problem bubbled to the surface as staff recruitment became more difficult. By the late 1960s, the NUR had become increasingly concerned that there had been considerable relaxation in the standard of qualifications required by the AEU for the granting of a craftsman's ticket and that staff were being recruited to the Works as craftsmen who were no more qualified than semi-skilled men working on mechanical tasks at Acton. In an effort to compromise on this situation the management said that they would require non-indentured craftsmen recruited from outside LT to take a trade test. This was different from any previous arrangement with the AEU and they were not prepared to accept it. The whole matter came to a head when the AEU called a strike of their members in October 1969, following what had seemed, at the time, to be only a minor dispute.

The strike caused considerable disruption to the Underground. The repair work carried out on the compressors fitted to 1938 Tube Stock, known as the KLL4 type, required a high output in mechanical fitting man-hours. These machines were a serious source of failure and needed a constant turnover of machines through the Works in order to maintain sufficient 1938 Stock trains for service. The strike saw all this work stop and it resulted in a rapid collapse in the availability of stock on the Northern and Bakerloo Lines.

Escalators also suffered as a result of this strike. Mechanical work was essential for the maintenance of escalators and this period saw a considerable increase in the number of escalators out of service all over the Underground. The strike lasted for almost three months and was the worst in the whole history of the Works. A formula was finally found for the resumption of work on 22nd December 1969.

As was the case throughout the industrial community in Britain, discipline during the early years at Acton Works was very strict. When the Works was first established, smoking and tea breaks were prohibited. Smoking was surreptitiously carried on in the toilets and tea was made and consumed illegally by all those who had some access to a heating device, such as a blacksmith's forge, a bunsen burner or an acetylene blow torch. Those operatives who had access to such amenities were always popular with their colleagues.

Although tea brewing was forbidden, it was recognised as unstoppable and even condoned by the foremen and chargehands. Eventually, it was officially recognised and, from 1928, tea barrows were allowed to move around the works to provide refreshment. Staff had to provide their own mugs and, of course, the service was not free. As a result, it did not entirely eliminate the illegal tea making and stories are legion of billy cans being allowed to burn out or of them being kicked down pits to avoid the owners being identified by supervisors on the prowl.

For a time after the introduction of the tea barrows, tea breaks were still not allowed. Tea had to be taken at the benches as convenient. Later, however, tea points were constructed in each shop and staff were given official ten minute tea breaks, one in the morning and one in the afternoon. The morning tea break eventually became unofficially lengthened so that it was possible to cook and eat a very good fried breakfast during the a.m. 'tea break'.

Eventually, smoking was also permitted except for half an hour at the end of the shift and in certain shops like the Wood Shop and the Trimming Shop where there was a fire risk.

Staff had to 'clock in'. Only two minutes' lateness was permitted; anyone stamping their card three minutes or later was penalised a quarter of an hour's pay. In later years, lateness caused by the late arrival of certain trains at Acton Town was accepted as an excuse without penalty. This was, perhaps, a sad indictment of the quality of the train service which was considered normal from the early 1970s. After the introduction of the incentive bonus schemes, a five-minute washing time was allowed at the end of each shift.

Clothing lockers were not originally provided for the staff. Each operating area had a clothes hoist where the staff were allocated pegs upon which they had to hang their outdoor clothes. The hoists were hauled up into the roof space immediately after clocking-on time and were not normally lowered until washing time. This system lasted for many years and was only replaced as the shops were modernised.

The raising and lowering of the hoists was the duty of one of the labourers but it was strictly controlled by the foreman of the section. The arrangement had two advantages, apart from the obvious one of preventing early departures. There was no pilfering from clothes and, under adverse weather conditions, the outdoor coats were properly aired by 'knocking off' time.

The need to lower a hoist at an unusual time could be embarrassing to the member of staff concerned. A tradition developed, known as 'banging out', when anyone requiring to leave early was given a send off of tools or noisy objects being banged as he left. The tradition originated around special occasions such as a retirement or a transfer to give a workmate a good send off, but any early departure was fair game as it was impossible for the hoist to be lowered without the whole shop being aware of it. The greater the likely embarrassment, the greater the noise of the 'banging out', especially if there was a bunch of flowers in evidence.

Originally, staff were not provided with overalls. They were expected to provide their own. In later years, however, pressure to provide some sort of help in those jobs which were excessively dirty, like the Blow Out Shop, led to special clothing being provided. Eventually, staff in these areas were paid additional 'dirty money' and had their own lockers and a changing room.

Exterior and interior views of the new Equipment Overhaul Workshop, completed in 1989. The interior view shows the despatch area. LUL

THE NEW ACTON WORKS

By 1930, the car maintenance and overhaul process on the Underground had settled down to a system which was to remain intact, apart from the war years, for over 50 years. Initially, cars were given a three-daily examination, a more detailed three-weekly inspection, and a two-yearly overhaul. The overhaul period was largely tied to the paint life and improvements in paint quality made it possible to extend this to three years by the late 1930s.

With the advent of the new stocks in the 1935-40 period, the maintenance periods were gradually extended so that, after the post-war reorganisation, they had been lengthened to an average, respectively, of five days, four weeks and four years. The four-yearly overhaul was equivalent to roughly 200,000 miles of running. The extension of time/mileage between overhauls had been due to both the conditions of reduced labour availability during the war and the discovery that overhaul periods could be extended for the newer stocks because of their relatively good condition, and for older stocks because the improved paint quality gave it a longer life.

By the end of the 1950s, the maintenance periods had been extended further to seven days, six weeks and five years. This was made possible partly by the introduction of 'programme lifting' in depots. It was first tried on the Central Line in the mid-1950s and was soon adopted all over the system. The purpose of the 'programme lift' was to ensure that bogies, wheels and motors were given regular attention, particularly now that overhaul periods were so extended.

Further extensions of maintenance periods were achieved with the continued reduction in wearing parts, especially with the introduction of rubber suspension units on the aluminium-bodied stocks of the 1960s. In the early 1970s, although examinations remained at intervals of seven days, inspections went out to nine weeks for older stocks and 18 weeks for the 1967 Tube and later stocks. Programme lifts were carried out at periods ranging from nine months for 1938 Tube Stock to two years for the 1967 Tube Stock. Overhauls were now at six-yearly intervals. These periods were extended even further by the late 1970s, with new stocks being designed with equipment which allowed them to operate without maintenance between 14-daily examinations, 15- to 30-weekly inspections and four-yearly programme lifts. Overhauls were to be extended to nine years. Today, new stocks are being planned with a single overhaul at 18 years of life.

During this time, with such rapid and accelerating reductions in maintenance requirements, the throughput of cars at Acton had fallen from 23 per week in 1948 to 18 per week in 1955 and to nine per week in 1980. However, the capacity of the Works remained at the 1928 level of 30 cars per week. The same reductions in maintenance requirements were also leaving over-capacity at the depots.

At sixty years old, Acton was in need of considerable modernisation to make it capable of handling future rolling stock efficiently. Less mechanical work and more emphasis on electronic equipment had changed the whole nature of rolling stock maintenance. In addition, there were difficulties in handling the longer cars introduced with the 1973 Tube Stock.

An initial survey into car overhaul was carried out in 1981 and a more detailed survey of the whole Works and its overhaul procedures was undertaken in 1983. It was done with the intention of reviewing the whole overhaul programme to ensure that unnecessary costs were not being incurred just because the facilities were there.

Shortly after these reviews were carried out, major political changes were introduced in the way London Transport was being managed. As a result, on 29th June 1984, the London Transport Executive, which had been under the control of the Greater London Council since 1970, was abolished and was replaced by a new body known as London Regional Transport (LRT). LRT now reported directly to the Department of Transport, whose terms of reference were more orientated to extracting value for money spent, rather than service to the public at any cost. Improved cost effectiveness was now regarded as of paramount importance and competitive tendering for work throughout the organisation quickly became mandatory, even if the work could be done in-house. On the Underground, the plans for streamlining the rolling stock overhaul system were now given considerable priority.

The studies carried out on car overhaul eventually concluded that overhaul could be dealt with at depots and that only those items of train equipment which needed specialist facilities should be sent elsewhere for overhaul or repair. The 'elsewhere' could mean Acton, which was to become the 'internal contractor', or an external contractor if they could provide a more competitive service.

The new plan was quickly accepted and the first stages put into operation. To prove that depots could carry out the required overhauls, trials were carried out at Golders Green beginning in March 1985. The first unit to have an overhaul completed away from Acton was a 3-car 1959 Tube Stock unit (1150). This was followed soon after by a 3-car 1972 unit (3463).

The trials at Golders Green were considered a success and arrangements were made for the overhauls of all other lines to be carried out at the depots. At two depots, Northfields and Hammersmith, it was realised that there was insufficient space to accommodate a unit in the workshop for long periods and allow normal maintenance work to be carried out. For this reason, it was decided that 1973 Tube Stock would be overhauled at Cockfosters and C Stock at Upminster.

Other depots involved in overhaul work were Neasden (A Stock), Ealing Common (D Stock), Ruislip (1962 Tube Stock), Northumberland Park (1967 Tube Stock), Stonebridge Park (all 1972 Stock) and Golders Green (1959 Tube Stock).

Henceforth, Acton Works, in its traditional form, was gradually run down. Train overhauls were progressively moved out to the depots so that, by April 1986, normal heavy overhaul work at Acton had ceased. By this time, Acton was carrying out the One-person-operation conversion work on the Metropolitan Line's A Stock. This had been won by competitive tender, the first major work to be allocated to Acton under the new system.

The studies into the Acton Works site and its uses culminated in a plan for a completely new approach. The Works was to be re-equipped at a cost of £15m to enable it to become a factory capable of carrying out component repairs and overhauls in competition with outside industry. A new workshop was to be built and new working practices introduced.

Detailed agreements were entered into with the trade unions which gave a simplified grading structure. Working groups, with two grades of craftsmen and semi-skilled workers, were set up, with each group under the control of a working chargehand. Sections of the workshop were to be under the supervision of a manager responsible for his own area and its finances.

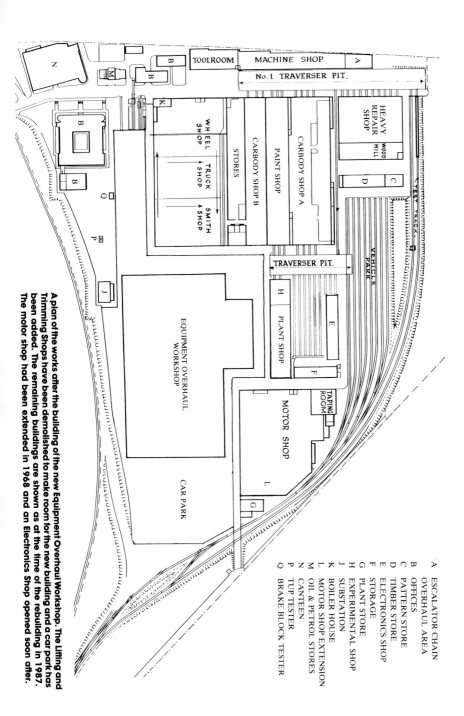

A plan of the works after the building of the new Equipment Overhaul Workshop. The Lifting and Trimming Shops have been demolished to make room for the new building and a car park has been added. The remaining buildings are shown as at the time of the rebuilding in 1987. The motor shop had been extended in 1968 and an Electronics Shop opened soon after.

TOOLROOM **MACHINE SHOP** A

No. 1 TRAVERSER PIT.

HEAVY REPAIR SHOP

WOOD MILL

D   C

WHEEL SHOP

TRUCK SHOP

SMITH SHOP

STORES

CARBODY SHOP B

PAINT SHOP

CARBODY SHOP A

K

TEST TRACK

TRAVERSER PIT.

VEHICLE PARK

H   PLANT SHOP

E

F

EQUIPMENT OVERHAUL WORKSHOP

CAR PARK

MOTOR SHOP

TAPING ROOM

L

G

J

P

O

N

B

M

B

B

B

A ESCALATOR CHAIN OVERHAUL AREA
B OFFICES
C PATTERN STORE
D TIMBER STORE
E ELECTRONICS SHOP
F STORAGE
G PLANT STORE
H EXPERIMENTAL SHOP
J SUBSTATION
K BOILER HOUSE
L MOTOR SHOP EXTENSION
M OIL & PETROL STORES
N CANTEEN
P TUP TESTER
O BRAKE BLOCK TESTER

77

The ability of staff to perform a category of work in the semi-skilled and craftsman grades would be determined by test, except for those having had a full apprenticeship. The flexibility between work areas allowed cover to be provided for temporary increases in workload and staff were expected to work below their normal level of competence if necessary. These agreements were instrumental in allowing the new workshop to operate within the new regime of value for money.

To achieve the new productivity goals, it was necessary to build new workshops. Following the transfer of overhaul work to the depots in 1986, the former lifting and trimming shops were demolished. The trimming work was transferred to a temporary site in the east end of what had been Carbody 'A', while any future car lifting was only possible by the use of a set of jacks, newly provided in the old Carbody 'B' Shop. Work commenced in January 1987 on the construction of a new Equipment Overhaul Works. The following work areas were provided:

Rotating Machines; including traction motors, compressors and motor alternators but excluding the capability for rewinding. This is specialist work and is not needed regularly. It was preferable to have it carried out by specialist contractors.

Wheelset Maintenance; including re-wheeling, re-axleing and gear replacement, plus motor suspension tube repairs but not wheel turning. The wheel turning was intended from the start to be carried out by modern copying lathes installed at Neasden, Ealing Common and Golders Green. All spoked wheels were replaced by monoblock wheels by 1991, thereby eliminating the necessity for retyring.

Trimming; with the whole fleet requiring retrimming over a period of nine to twelve years.

Electrical and Mechanical; including assemblies such as electrical switchgear and pneumatic valves plus items like automatic couplers requiring overhaul at periods of up to nine years.

Electronic Maintenance; including malfunction analysis, repair and modification. This type of work has expanded in recent years with the proliferation of electronic devices on rolling stock.

Support; including welding, sheet metal work and a blacksmith working on a one-off, jobbing basis.

Machining and Tool Production; providing support for all sections of the new workshop and the depots, including the manufacture of replacement parts as necessary.

Work which was considered outside the scope of the new facility included truck overhaul and wheel profiling. Modern wheel lathes were provided at the larger depots and other depots could ship wheels by road for reprofiling when required. The volume of work was such on modern rolling stock that this was not perceived as causing great difficulties.

A new type of mini-container was designed for the transfer of equipment by road between Acton and the depots. A container could contain all the seats from a car, for example, or pieces of electrical equipment as required.

Detailed examination showed that it would be practicable to relocate the required activities into some of the vacated workshop space at Acton. However, the layout which resulted was very inefficient in the use of the space and it had been hoped that some released space might be profitably converted for use in other ways. It was therefore decided that it would be better to build new premises.

Work began on the new Equipment Overhaul Works (EOW), as the new shops at Acton are called, in January 1987 when the former lifting and trimming shops were razed to the ground. The work took two years and cost £22 million. The EOW now employs fewer than 400 staff. The view above shows the overhaul area for pneumatic camshaft mechanism (PCM) equipment whilst the picture below a computer-controlled lathe. LUL

Having decided the size of the new facility, it was found possible to fit the new workshop within the existing works boundary and to allow work of some kind to continue there in the meantime. This allowed employment on the site to continue during the rebuilding phase. The transfer of overhaul work to the depots released some space, while the heavy repair and major modification work continued at Acton and gave the continued employment link. It was intended that eventually the heavy repair work would be transferred to a new facility to be constructed at Ealing Common.

The Equipment Overhaul Works at Acton is now fully operational and overhaul of cars is now all done at depots. Those parts of the original works at Acton which have survived owe their continued existence to the fire at King's Cross. Following that event, there was a decision to modify all existing rolling stock to a higher level of fire resistance and to prevent passenger alarm operation from stopping the train. Public address was also to be installed in all trains.

The work was to be carried out at such a speed that it was impossible for the existing facilities at Acton and the depots to cope and both internal and external contracting facilities were used. BREL was contracted to do the 1962 Tube Stock at Derby and Crewe while the 1959 Tube Stock was carried out at a temporary facility at Highgate Depot by TB Precision. The 1967/72 Tube Stocks were done at Acton in a much reduced part of the original works by what has become known as the Train Modification Unit (TMU), the 'internal contractor'. With that job completed, the TMU started on engineering modifications to the 1973 Tube Stock. When that is finished, it is planned to sever the rail connection with the District Line at Acton Town and build a new training centre over the tracks.

It might be said that the beginning of the end for Acton Works was the large scale introduction of unpainted bodies for Underground rolling stock in the early 1960s. The scourge of graffiti and the damage it has done to the external finish of car bodies has led to a decision to paint the exteriors of all future stock. Much of the existing stock will also be painted under the refurbishment plans now just beginning.

The paint used for the repainting work will be a new graffiti resistant combination. It requires special installation and protection facilities. The work is being carried out by specialist contractors at Leicester and Doncaster. It is likely, however, that the Underground will need to provide a special painting facility in the future in order to be able to repaint cars on a regular basis.

It remains to be seen if the abandonment of the central overhaul system for rolling stock on the Underground was the right decision. Whilst the old facility at Acton was outmoded and was overdue for modernisation, it performed a useful service. It acted as a maintainer of standards across the system, it pooled the expertise needed to carry out railway overhaul and modification work, it acted as a 'long stop' for depot maintenance, ensuring that work skimped or missed was picked up upon overhaul, and it provided a centre for railway engineering design and experience. It might be said that all this has been lost in the progression towards business efficiency in the short term without sufficient emphasis being placed upon the long term requirements of the railway as a whole.